Antennas for VHF
and above

Edited by

Ian Poole, G3YWX

RSGB

Radio Society of Great Britain

Published by the Radio Society of Great Britain, 3 Abbey Court, Priory Business Park, Bedford, MK44 3WH

First Published 2008

ISBN 9781 9050 8645 0

Publisher's note
The opinions expressed in this book are those of the authors and not necessarily those of the RSGB. While the information presented is believed to be correct, the authors, the publisher and their agents cannot accept responsibility for the consequences arising for any inaccuracies or omissions.

Cover designer: Kim Meyern
Subeditor: George Brown, MW5ACN
Typography: Chris Danby, G0DWV.
Production: Mark Allgar, M1MPA

Printed in Great Britain by Latimer Trend of Plymouth

This book has a supporting website:

http://www.rsgb.org/books/extra/VHFantennas.htm

Any corrections and points of clarification that have not been incorporated in this printing of the book can be found here along with any supporting material that may have become available

Contents

Chapter 8
Microwave Antennas 97

Chapter 9
Antenna Measurements 109

Chapter 10
Practical Aspects 125

Index

Preface

Antennas are fascinating to read about and then to build. They are items that most people have a good chance of building successfully. While it is often not practicable to build many of the more electronics-orientated items of equipment such as transceivers, this is not the case for antennas. Constructing the station antennas gives a sense of pride, in that the station is more than just a series of commercially-made items that have been connected together. This is not the only benefit, because the antenna can be tailored to meet the needs of the station and the performance of the whole station can be improved by ensuring that the antenna is optimised and performing to its best.

In some cases, building the antenna may save some money, but this may not always be the case. Part of the enjoyment of the hobby comes from building things and taking on new challenges. It also helps in learning about radio in general and, after all, one of the aims of the amateur radio licence is self-training in radio.

While cost and enjoyment can be reasons for building antennas, some types are not easily available. Parabolic reflectors used for some of the microwave applications are not widely available as amateur radio products and there is little option but to build them or to modify antennas originally intended for other applications.

In this book, I hope to bring out the enjoyment of investigating different types of antenna and building some of them. I have used my previous book *Antennas for VHF and UHF* as the basis and added new material to it, and have brought in some additional designs that have appeared elsewhere, especially in the area of what may be termed microwave antennas.

In preparing this book as editor I have naturally had help from others. First of all, thanks to those whose designs have been used. I have endeavoured to give credit in the text to all whose designs appear there. In addition to this, Alun Cross, G4WGE, has helped with discussions and reading various sections of the book, and Andy Barter, G8ATD, provided the parabolic reflector design.

However most of all, I hope that you enjoy reading the book, that you find it useful; it may give you some ideas for constructing antennas!

Ian Poole
August 2008

Chapter 1
Basic Concepts

In this Chapter
- ELECTROMAGNETIC WAVES
- POLARISATION
- THE ANTENNA SYSTEM
- OPERATION OF AN ANTENNA
- ANTENNA FEED IMPEDANCE
- DIRECTIVITY
- ANTENNA GAIN
- ANGLE OF RADIATION
- BANDWIDTH
- STACKING AND BAYING ANTENNAS

Most radio amateurs find antennas fascinating. Part of the reason for this is that they are crucial to the overall performance of any station. A poor antenna will limit a station's performance, regardless of the other equipment that is used, but a good antenna will bring much better results and enable the performance of the rest of the station to be improved.

In view of their importance, many people enjoy experimenting with antennas, improving their performance and trying out new ideas. Time and effort spent on an antenna is rarely wasted. Not only can a great amount be leaned, but the improvements that are gained make the time spent very satisfying.

To achieve the best results from an antenna, it is obviously helpful to have an understanding of how it works. An in-depth study involves serious mathematical analysis. Fortunately, this is not necessary for most amateur work. Instead, a good understanding of the concepts and techniques is all that is usually needed.

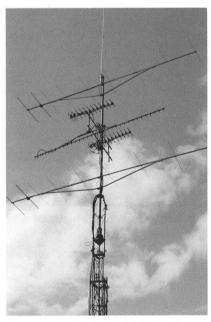

An impressive VHF / UHF Antenna system.

ELECTROMAGNETIC WAVES

The purpose of an antenna is to receive and transmit radio signals. Radio waves are electromagnetic (E/M) waves, like light, X-rays and ultraviolet rays. These waves are made up from two constituents: an electric field and a magnetic field that are inseparable from one another. As shown in **Fig 1.1** they are at right angles to one another. It can be scientifically shown that the energy in the wave is divided equally between the electric and magnetic constituents.

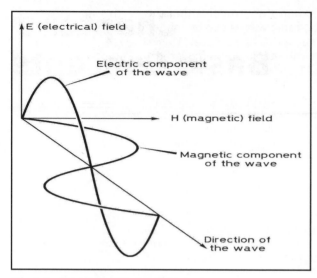

Fig 1.1: An electromagnetic wave.

A number of points can be noted about an electromagnetic wave. The first is the wavelength. This is the distance between the same point on two successive waves. Normally the crest is chosen as a good example to visualise, though any point can be chosen. The wavelength may vary from many hundreds or thousands of metres to less than a millimetre. **Fig 1.2**

Another feature of an electromagnetic wave is its velocity. Being the same as a light wave it has the same velocity. Normally this is taken to be **3 x 10⁸** metres per second (m/s or ms⁻¹) although a more exact figure is 299,792,500ms⁻¹ in a vacuum.

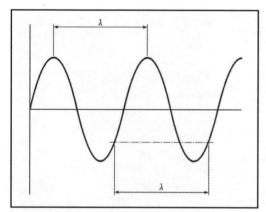

Fig 1.2: The wavelength of a wave.

The third fact that can be noted about a wave is its frequency of vibration. In the early days of wireless the wavelength of a signal was used to determine its position on a radio dial. Today the frequency is used. This gives a far more accurate and useful representation. It is also much easier to measure very accurately. The standard unit of frequency is the Hertz, where one Hertz (Hz) corresponds to one cycle per second (c/s). As radio frequencies can be very high, the standard prefixes of kilo (kilohertz, kHz) for a thousand Hertz, Mega (Megahertz, MHz) for a million Hertz, and Giga (Gigahertz, GHz) for a thousand million Hertz, are commonly used.

There is a very simple mathematical relationship between the velocity, frequency and wavelength of an electromagnetic wave:

Frequency x Wavelength = Velocity

or more commonly where f is expressed in Hertz and λ in metres:

$$f \times \lambda = 3 \times 10^8 .$$

The way in which electromagnetic waves travel is of great interest. If the wave is pictured as originating at a point in space, the wave spreads out in an ever-expanding sphere with the source at the centre. The path of the energy from the source to any point on the sphere is a straight line, in space, and these lines are often thought of as 'rays'. However, there are many ways in which these 'rays' can be bent or reflected so that they follow a different course, especially when they travel within the earth's atmosphere. By utilising these effects, radio waves can be made to travel over enormous distances around the earth's surface. This study of propagation is beyond the scope of this book but is covered in *Radio Propagation: Principles and Practice* [1].

POLARISATION

It is a well known fact that light waves can be polarised. Very basically this means that the vibrations occur in a particular plane. One analogy for this could be seen when a piece of string is made to vibrate. If it only vibrated up and down then it would be said to be vertically polarised. As an electromagnetic wave has two constituents, the polarisation is taken to be that of the *electric* field.

The polarisation of a radio wave is very important because it is found that an antenna will radiate a signal having a particular polarisation. Similarly, when receiving, the received signal will be maximum when the polarisation of the antenna is the same as that of the incoming signal.

For most antennas it is quite easy to determine the polarisation. It is simply the same plane as that containing the elements of the antenna. So a vertical antenna (ie one with vertical elements) will receive vertically-polarised signals best and, similarly, a horizontal antenna will give optimum performance with horizontally-polarised signals.

Vertical and horizontal polarisation both fall into a category known as *linear polarisation*. However, it is also possible to use *circular polarisation*. This has a number of benefits for areas such as satellite applications where it helps to overcome propagation anomalies, ground reflections and the effects of the spin of many satellites. It is a little more difficult to visualise the effect of circular polarisation than linear polarisation. Try imagining a signal propagating from a dipole antenna that is rotating. The tip of the electric field vector will then be seen to trace out a corkscrew as it travels away from the antenna. Circular polarisation can be seen to be either right or left handed, dependent upon the direction of rotation as seen from the transmitter.

Elliptical polarisation occurs when there is a mix of linear and circular polarisation. This can be visualised as before by the tip of the electric field vector tracing out an elliptically-shaped corkscrew.

In free space, once a signal has been transmitted its polarisation will remain the same. So in order to receive the maximum signal, the transmitting and receiving antennas must be in the same plane. If for any reason their polarisations are perpendicular to one another (ie cross-polarised), in theory no signal would be received. Similarly for circular polarisation, a right-handed circularly-polarised antenna will not receive a left-hand circularly-polarised signal. However a dipole (which is a linearly-polarised antenna) *will* be able to receive a circularly-polarised signal. The strength will be equal whether the dipole is mounted vertically, horizontally or in any other plane at right angles to the incoming signal, but it will be 3dB less (half power) than if a circularly-polarised antenna of the same sense is used.

For real applications on earth, it is found that, once a signal has been transmitted, its polarisation will remain broadly the same. However, reflections from objects in the path can change the polarisation and, as the received signal will be the sum of the direct signal plus a number of reflected signals, the overall polarisation of the signal can change slightly.

Linearly-polarised beam antennas (such as a Yagi) that have complicated polar diagrams may radiate side lobes that have signals with a polarisation different from that of the main beam. They may be linearly polarised, or even elliptical and, as a result, cross-polarised signals may be more strongly received with the beam directed away from the source of the received signal.

Horizontal, vertical and circular polarisations are all used at VHF and UHF. Conventionally, FM operation uses vertical polarisation. The reason for this arises mainly from the need not to re-orientate the direction of an antenna during mobile or hand-portable operation. Many vertical antennas have an omnidirectional radiation pattern in the horizontal plane, ie the signal strength around the antenna is equal in all horizontal directions. It would clearly be unacceptable for a mobile station to have to redirect an antenna whilst in motion. Most packet radio operation also uses vertical polarisation.

Horizontal polarisation is almost always used for long-distance work. This is mainly because it is more difficult to mount a vertically-polarised Yagi antenna on a metallic support without affecting its radiating pattern. However, horizontal polarisation does offer some advantages in signal propagation. This arises from the way in which signals are scattered and diffracted by the ground or refracted by the troposphere.

Circular polarisation is used for satellite communications, although it is by no means a requirement. As already mentioned there are advantages in terms of propagation and in overcoming the fading caused if the satellite is spinning. However, the drawback is that the polarisation may be opposite to that of the receiving antenna in which case the received signal will be much reduced. This is likely to be much less than the signal produced by a linearly-polarised antenna. While it is possible to switch the direction of circular polarisation, this considerably adds to the cost of the antenna system.

THE ANTENNA SYSTEM
A complete antenna system is made up from more than just the antenna element itself, although this is obviously the central part of the whole setup. In addition, there are other items, such as the feeder that is used to transfer the energy to and from the antenna. Feeders are needed because the optimum situation for the antenna is seldom at the same place as the equipment.

Other items may also needed. These could include a matching system which might be required when the antenna impedance does not match that of the feeder. This often happens when more than one antenna is fed from a single feeder, or when a balun is required. Both of these instances are described in Chapter 2. All of these items form part of the overall antenna system.

OPERATION OF AN ANTENNA

The way in which an antenna operates is quite complicated. Fortunately, a full understanding is rarely necessary, and a simple explanation will give a broad qualitative understanding of its function. Essentially, there is an RF current flowing in the antenna and this generates the magnetic part of the electromagnetic wave. The electric constituent is generated automatically by the varying charge.

It is interesting to note that, close to the antenna, there is also an inductive field, the same as that in a transformer. This is not part of the electromagnetic wave, but it can distort measurements close to the antenna. It can also mean that breakthrough interference is more likely when a

A six-metre array used for the 9M0C DXpedition to the Spratly Islands.

transmitting antenna is close to other antennas or wiring that might have the signal induced into it. A receiving antenna is more susceptible to interference from domestic equipment if it is close to house wiring and the like. Fortunately, this inductive field reduces fairly rapidly with distance and is barely detectable at distances beyond about two or three wavelengths from the antenna.

ANTENNA FEED IMPEDANCE

The impedance presented at the feed-point of an antenna is very important and it is called the *feed impedance*. It is necessary to ensure there is a good match between the feeder and the antenna to ensure the maximum power transfer between the two.

The feed impedance of the antenna results from a number of factors, including the size and shape of the antenna, the frequency of operation and its environment. The impedance is normally complex, ie consisting of resistive as well as reactive components. The resistive components are made up from two parts. One is the 'loss resistance' of the elements. This should be maintained as low as possible to prevent any power being dissipated as heat and not being radiated. The other resistive component of the impedance is the 'radiation resistance'. This can be thought of as a virtual resistor. It arises from the fact that power is 'dissipated' when it is radiated. There are also reactive components of the feed impedance. These come from the antenna elements acting as tuned circuits that possess inductance and capacitance. At resonance, where most antennas are operated, the inductance and capacitance cancel one another out to leave only the combined radiation resistance and loss resistance. However, either side of resonance, the feed impedance quickly becomes either inductive (if operated below the resonant frequency) or capacitive (if operated above the resonant frequency).

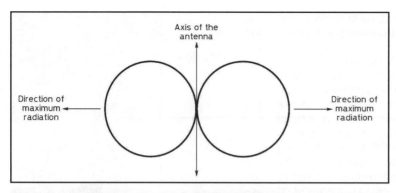

Fig 1.3: A polar diagram for a dipole antenna, showing that the radiation peaks at right angles to the line of the antenna.

DIRECTIVITY

The radiation from a practical antenna is not the same in all directions. In fact, the intensity of the radiation varies around the antenna from place to place, and a plot of this is called its radiation pattern. As the radiation varies in three planes a full three-dimensional representation would be ideal, but normally this is not required. Instead, a diagram known as a *polar diagram* is used to plot the performance of the antenna in a particular plane. Essentially, this plots a curve around an antenna showing the intensity of the radiation at each point. Normally, a logarithmic scale is used so that the differences can be conveniently seen on the plot. An example of a dipole antenna is shown in **Fig 1.3**.

Different antennas radiate differently and therefore produce different polar diagrams. An omni-directional antenna is one which radiates equally (or approximately equally) in all directions in the plane of interest. An antenna that radiates equally in all directions in all planes is called an isotropic antenna. It is not possible to create one in reality, but it is a useful imaginary reference for some measurements. Other antennas will exhibit highly directional patterns, and these can be put to good use in many applications. The popular Yagi antenna is used in many areas of amateur, commercial and domestic applications. In fact virtually all terrestrial television antennas are of this type.

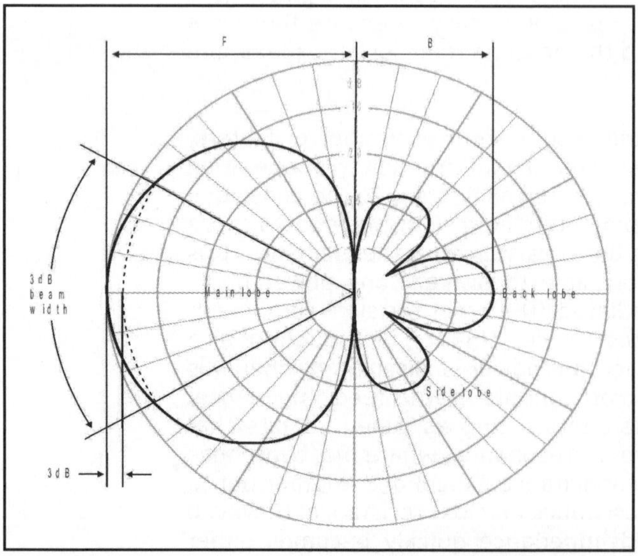

Like the radiation pattern for a typical Yagi antenna shown in **Fig 1.4**, many antennas have a radiation pattern that varies around the antenna. There are several key features that can be seen from the polar diagram. The first is that there is a *main beam* or *lobe* and a number of *minor lobes*. It is often useful to define the beamwidth of an antenna, to indicate how much of the radiation is concentrated in one direction. This is taken to be

Fig 1.4: A typical polar diagram for a Yagi antenna, showing how more power is 'focused' in one direction than another.

angle between the two points where the power falls to half its maximum level, and as a result it is sometimes called the half-power beamwidth.

ANTENNA GAIN

The *gain* of an antenna is important and will often be specified. It is defined as a ratio of the signal transmitted in the 'maximum-power' direction compared with that of a standard or reference antenna. The resultant ratio is then normally expressed in decibels (dB). In theory, the standard antenna could be almost anything, but two types are normally used. The most common is a simple dipole as it is easily available and is the basis of many other types of antenna. In this case the gain is expressed as dBd, ie the gain expressed in decibels compared with a dipole. However, a dipole does not radiate equally in all directions in all planes, so a theoretical *isotropic* source is sometimes used as the basis for comparison. In this case the gain is specified in dBi, ie gain in decibels compared with an isotropic source. The main drawback with using an isotropic source as a reference is that it is not possible to make a perfect version of one, so figures using it can only be theoretical. However, it is possible to relate the two, as a dipole has a gain of 2.1dB over an isotropic source, ie 2.1dBi. In other words, figures expressed as gain over an isotropic source will be 2.1dB higher than those relative to a dipole. When choosing an antenna and looking at the gain specifications, be sure to check whether the gain is relative to a dipole or an isotropic source.

An impressive array of VHF, UHF and microwave antennas

Apart from the forward gain of an antenna, another important parameter is the *front-to-back* ratio. This is expressed in decibels and, as the name implies, it is the ratio of the maximum signal in the forward direction to the signal in the opposite direction (F/B in Fig 1.4). The design of an antenna can be adjusted to give either maximum forward gain *or* maximum front-to-back ratio, as the two do not normally coincide exactly. For most amateur VHF and UHF operation, the design is normally optimised for forward gain, as this gives the maximum radiated signal in the required direction.

So far all the reasoning about directivity in antennas has applied to the case when an antenna is used for transmitting. The same reasoning can also be applied when an antenna is used for receiving; the antenna will be able to pick up signals in one direction better than another, and better than an antenna with no directivity. This has two effects. The first is that any interfering signals coming from a direction different from the wanted one can be reduced in strength, and the second is that the antenna gain can be used to increase the strength of the wanted signal. This can be particularly useful when trying to receive signals that are of minimal strength.

It is worth noting that the higher the gain of a particular type of antenna, the narrower its beamwidth. It becomes very important with high-gain antennas to ensure that they can be accurately set in the correct direction otherwise some of the power will be directed wrongly and wasted. Similarly, fewer stations may be heard, as only stations in the direction of the antenna main lobe will be enhanced in strength. Those signals not within the beamwidth will be reduced in strength.

ANGLE OF RADIATION

Another aspect of directivity is the angle of radiation. Essentially, this is the radiation pattern in the vertical plane. This is determined by taking the angle between the ground and the direction in which most of the radiation emanates from the antenna. An antenna is said to have a low angle of radiation if the main lobe is parallel to the ground. Conversely, an antenna with a high angle of radiation will have much of its power directed upwards. For most VHF and UHF antennas it is necessary to have a low angle of radiation so that the signal is directed towards the horizon and can be heard by stations at ground level. Unlike the HF bands, signals on frequencies above about 100MHz will generally not be reflected back by the ionosphere so anything radiated at a high angle will be wasted.

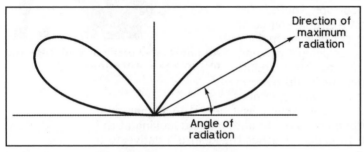

Fig 1.5: Angle of radiation.

The angle of radiation is determined by a number of factors. The main one is obviously the antenna itself. Some antennas will be able to concentrate more of their power at a low angle because of their directive nature. A basic horizontal antenna with little or no directivity, such as a dipole will not be particularly good. However, vertical antennas are very much better as shown in **Fig 1.5** because the maximum radiation is at right angles to the axis of the antenna.

BANDWIDTH

An antenna has certain bandwidths over which it can operate satisfactorily. The two major determining factors are the impedance and the beamwidth. Accordingly, both impedance bandwidth and radiation pattern bandwidth are specified.

One major feature of an antenna that changes with frequency is its impedance. This can cause the amount of reflected power to increase. If the antenna is used for transmitting, damage may be caused either to the transmitter or to the feeder beyond a given level of reflected power. This is quite likely to limit the operating bandwidth of the antenna. Today, most transmitters have some form of VSWR protection circuit that prevents damage by reducing the output power to an acceptable level as the levels of reflected power increase. However, this means that the efficiency of the station is reduced if it is operated outside a given bandwidth. For receiving, the impedance changes of the antenna are not as critical, but the efficiency will still fall. For amateur operation, the acceptable bandwidth is often taken as the range of frequencies within which a VSWR figure no greater than 1.5:1 is produced.

The radiation pattern is also frequency-dependent, and this is particularly noticeable in the case of a beam. In particular, the front-to-back ratio will fall off rapidly outside a given bandwidth, and so will the gain. In an antenna such as a Yagi, this is caused by a reduction in the currents in the parasitic elements (reflector and directors) when the frequency of operation is moved away from resonance. For this type of beam, the radiation pattern bandwidth is defined as the frequency range over which the gain of the main lobe is within 1dB of its maximum.

A number of measures can be taken to increase an antenna's bandwidth. One is the use of thicker conductors. Another is the type of antenna used. For example, a folded dipole (described fully in Chapter 3) has a wider bandwidth than a non-folded one. In fact, by looking at a standard television antenna it is possible to see both of these features included.

For many beam antennas - especially high-gain ones - the impedance bandwidth is wider than the radiation pattern bandwidth, although the two parameters are inter-related in many respects.

STACKING AND BAYING ANTENNAS
In order to improve the gain of an antenna system, two individual antennas may be used, and the power split between them. The most common method is to place one above the other (stacking), but it is also possible to place them side-by-side (baying). This can increase the gain of the antenna system as a whole. To achieve the improvement in gain the beamwidth is naturally reduced. Normally antennas are stacked. There are two reasons for this. The first is a practical consideration, and is because the vertical mounting pole facilitates the easier mounting of antennas above one another. Antennas that are bayed require more complicated mounting requirements. Secondly, stacking antennas reduces the beamwidth in the vertical plane, ensuring that main lobe parallel to the earth is narrower and there is less high-angle radiation. Baying antennas reduces the beamwidth in the horizontal plane, requiring more accurate beam settings.

Each antenna has what can be thought of as a 'collecting area'. This is called the *effective aperture* and, broadly speaking, it is the area over which the antenna collects the incident power. The larger the antenna gain and directivity, the greater is the area of the effective aperture. For anyone wishing to calculate the effective aperture, A_{eff}, the formula is given by:

$$A_{eff} = \frac{\lambda^2 G}{4\pi} ,$$

where λ is the wavelength in metres and G is the power gain of the antenna relative to an isotropic source (not in decibels but expressed as a factor). A half-wave dipole has a gain of 1.64 over an isotropic source.

It is important to know the effective aperture of each antenna when stacking and baying. If the effective apertures of two antennas overlap then they will share the power. This means that the maximum gain cannot be obtained.

A further reason why antennas cannot be placed too close together is that mutual coupling between the antenna elements affects both the radiation pattern and the feed impedance of the elements. In turn, this affects the gain that can be attained. As a result of this, even optimally-placed stacked or bayed antennas never achieve the maximum theoretical gain. The extent to which antennas affect one another is difficult to predict, but those with low side-lobe levels are obviously the best.

REFERENCES AND FURTHER READING

[1]   *Radio Propagation: Principles and Practice*, Ian Poole (RSGB)

[2]   Antenna picture on page 7 courtesy of G4WGE

Chapter 2
Feeders and Connectors

In this Chapter

The feeder and its associated connectors form an essential part of any antenna system. It serves to transfer the energy picked up by the antenna down to the receiver or, conversely, it transfers the power from the transmitter to the antenna. This has to be done with the minimum amount of power loss. The lengths of feeder can be fairly long in some instances. This is because the optimum position for an antenna is generally as high as possible and away from objects that are likely to act as screens. This means that it will be some distance away from the equipment connected to it. In view of this, the feeder plays an important role in the overall operation of the antenna system. A poor feeder will result in the whole antenna system being degraded. Conversely, a good feeder will ensure that the maximum amount of energy is transferred from the antenna to the receiver, or from the transmitter to the antenna.

The operation of a feeder is not quite as straightforward as one might expect from the first look. There are several parameters and characteristics that play a vital role in the operation of the feeder and need to be understood, at least in general terms.

CHARACTERISTIC IMPEDANCE

Just as an antenna has a value of impedance, and a receiver or transmitter has an input or output impedance, a feeder has what is called a *characteristic impedance*. This is expressed in ohms. It is very important because it is necessary to match the feeder's impedance to that of the rest of the system.

The impedance of the feeder is governed by a number of factors. Its physical dimensions have a very large bearing on it. Also the dielectric constant of the material between, and sometimes around, the feeder can vary the impedance. Fortunately, it is relatively easy to control these factors to a sufficient degree to make feeders with the right value of impedance.

Feeder impedance is very important. In order to achieve the optimum efficiency in an antenna system the antenna, the feeder and the transmitter or receiver should all have the same characteristic impedance, or have a matching network to ensure that they are all matched. The reason for this is that in any system the maximum power transfer takes place when the impedance of the source and the load are the same. If there is a 'mismatch' between the two, the efficiency is reduced.

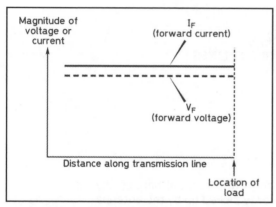

Fig 2.1: Voltage and current magnitude along a perfectly matched feeder.

STANDING WAVES

Feeders are used to transfer power from a source to a load. In the case where a signal is being transmitted, the source for the whole system is obviously the transmitter and the load is the antenna. When a signal is being received, the source is the antenna and the load is the input to the receiver. While people usually refer to standing waves with respect to a transmitted signal, an antenna system that has a high standing wave ratio will not be performing to its maximum efficiency and will therefore not operate well for receiving.

When a load is perfectly matched to the impedance of the feeder, the voltage and current magnitudes will be constant along the feeder as shown in **Fig 2.1**. However, when a load is not matched the situation is a little different. It has already been mentioned that for maximum power transfer from one item to another the impedance of the source and load must be the same. When looking at the transfer of the power from the feeder to the load, the feeder acts as the source. In this case the power enters the feeder and travels along it. If there is a poor match between the feeder and the load, only a proportion of the power can be transferred. The remaining power cannot disappear and is reflected back along the feeder. When this happens, the voltages and currents associated with the forward and the reflected power add and subtract in different places. The net result of this is that standing waves are set up and points of high and low current and voltage are generated.

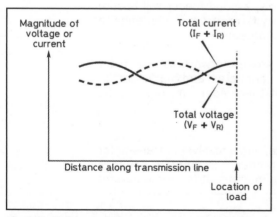

Fig 2.2: Voltage and current magnitudes along a feeder when the load impedance is lower than that of the feeder.

Fig 2.2 shows an example where a feeder is terminated by a load with a resistive impedance lower than the characteristic impedance of the feeder. From a simple application of Ohm's Law it can be seen that at the load the voltage is lower than if it had been a perfect match, while the current is higher. Further back down the feeder the voltage and current change. At a point an eighth of a wavelength away from the load the current has fallen to a minimum while the voltage has risen to a maximum. Then a quarter a wavelength away from the load the voltage is falling whilst the current has actually reached its minimum. This logic can be followed through until at a point half a wavelength away from the load, where the current and voltage are the same as at the load.

If the load resistance is higher than the characteristic impedance of the feeder, a similar situation exists, but the voltage and current phases are different. The current at the load would be lower than had it been perfectly terminated. Again, standing waves would be set up but the patterns would be those shown in **Fig 2.3**. NB - the diagrams show the situation for a small SWR.

When talking about standing waves it is useful to have a way of quantifying them. Generally, a factor called the *standing wave ratio* or SWR is used. It is the ratio of the maximum to minimum values on the line. The standing wave ratio can be calculated from a knowledge of these values

$$SWR = \frac{I_{max}}{I_{min}} = \frac{V_{max}}{V_{min}}.$$

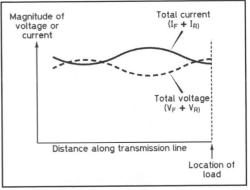

Fig 2.3: Voltage and current magnitudes along a feeder when the load impedance is higher than that of the feeder.

The standing wave ratio may have a range of values from unity to infinity. A perfectly-matched line will have a constant magnitude of voltage along the line and will have a unity SWR (expressed as 1:1). An open-circuit or short-circuit line will have minimum values that fall to zero and hence the value of SWR will rise to infinity (expressed as ∞:1). Normally, a standing wave ratio is expressed as a figure greater than unity, eg 4:1. It is easy to measure the voltage standing wave ratio (VSWR) using an inexpensive instrument and is an easy way to find out the performance of the antenna system. The general case for a resistive termination of a line is given below:

$$SWR = \frac{R}{Z_0} \text{ , when } R \text{ is greater than } Z_0 \text{, and}$$

$$SWR = \frac{Z_0}{R} \text{ , when } Z_0 \text{ is greater than } R.$$

R is the terminating resistance and Z_0 is the impedance of the line. It is worth noting that most antennas exhibit a load characteristic that is virtually all resistive at resonance, becoming reactive as the frequency moves away from resonance. In fact it becomes inductive below resonance and capacitive above resonance.

The standing wave ratio is also linked to the proportion of power that is reflected. This is generally called the reflection coefficient (ρ). The link between the two is quite easy to work out because the maximum of the standing wave will be the forward power, P, *plus* the reflected power, ie P(1+ρ) and the minimum will be the forward power *minus* the reflected power ie P(1-ρ). This means that the ratio of the two becomes

$$SWR = \frac{1+\rho}{1-\rho} \; .$$

The standing waves in themselves will not be a problem in a receiving system. They will obviously indicate a mismatch and loss of efficiency but no more than this. In a transmitting system they are more important. The high levels of current and voltage that may be seen by the power amplifier of the transmitter may cause the output devices to fail. To prevent this happening most transmitters have detection circuitry that reduces the power output when a high level of standing waves is detected. Accordingly, the transmitter will not be capable of delivering its full power output on a poorly-matched antenna system. Additionally, the points of high current can cause local heating that may be sufficient in some cases to deform the cable. Alternatively, the voltage peaks have been known to cause breakdown between the two conductors in the cable.

VELOCITY FACTOR

When a radio wave travels in free space it travels at the speed of light. It would also travel along a feeder at the same speed if it did not contain an insulating dielectric. As a result of the dielectric, the speed is reduced by a factor of $1/\varepsilon$ where ε is the *dielectric constant*. This is the velocity factor, or the proportion of the speed of light at which the wave travels in the feeder. Sometimes it can be as low as 0.6 but it is usually around 0.66 for most coaxial cables, and it can be as high as 0.98 for open-wire feeders, particularly those where there is no plastic dielectric all along the line.

In addition to the velocity changing, the wavelength of the signal in the feeder is reduced by the same factor. This is because the velocity of the wave is equal to the frequency times the wavelength and if the frequency is constant, but the velocity is changed, then so must the wavelength. Because the velocity changes, the wavelength of the signal in the feeder is also reduced by the velocity factor. For instance, one wavelength of a 100MHz signal in free space is 3m. At the same frequency, one wavelength in a feeder with a velocity factor of 0.66 is 2m (ie 0.66 x 3m). This is particularly important if a length of cable has to be cut to a specific number of wavelengths.

LOSS

The loss of a feeder cable is another very important factor. Obviously, in an ideal world, it would be possible to feed a certain amount of power into the cable at one end and expect to see the same amount at the other end. In reality, this is never the case. Each cable has a certain amount of loss and this is dependent upon many factors including the length. Normally the loss is expressed as a certain number of decibels over a certain length (eg in dB/m)

This loss is caused by a number of factors. One is the resistance of the wire, although at high frequencies the *skin effect* dominates. This means that the currents for the signal only travel close to the surface of the wire, which is why tubing can often be used for antenna elements. The resistance can be reduced by making the wires thicker and adding further conductors to increase the surface area available but this, in turn, means that the whole cable has to be made larger if the same impedance is to be maintained. This obviously puts up the cost. Power can also be lost in the dielectric material between the two conductors.

The loss of a cable is also dependent upon the frequency in use. It will rise as the frequency is increased. Accordingly the loss will be given for a number of different frequencies, and an intelligent guess or interpolation can be made for the particular frequency in use. However, be aware that care should be taken when extrapolating above the maximum frequency specified as the loss can rise dramatically.

The level of loss of a cable is of paramount importance in any antenna system, particularly when it comes to very sensitive receiver systems capable of picking up signals close to the noise level. In these circumstances, any signal lost cannot be regained by adding more amplification as the associated noise will be amplified as well. It is equally important for transmitting systems where power lost in the feeder is not radiated and this could make reception at a distant location much more difficult.

TYPES OF FEEDER

A number of different types of feeder can be used. Some are in common everyday use while others are seen only very occasionally. Each one has its own advantages and disadvantages, and applications to which it is best suited. Often the choice of which type of feeder to use is quite easy, but it is useful to know exactly what is available and so three of the more commonly used types are outlined here.

Coax

The most common type of feeder used today is undoubtedly *coaxial feeder* or 'coax'. As the name suggests the cable consists of two concentric conductors as shown in **Fig 2.4**. The centre conductor is almost always made of copper. Exceptions to this include LDF250 / LDF450 where the centre conductor is made from copper plate on steel. Sometimes it may be a single conductor while at other times it may consist of several strands.

The outer conductor is normally made from copper braid. This enables the cable to be flexible, which would not be the case if the outer conductor were

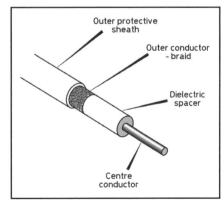

Fig 2.4 Coaxial feeder.

solid. To improve the screening, double- or even triple-screened cables are sometimes used. Normally, this is accomplished by placing one braid directly over another although, in some instances, a copper foil or tape shield may be used. By using additional layers of screening, the levels of stray pick-up and radiation are considerably reduced. More importantly for most radio amateurs, this will result in lower levels of loss.

Between the two conductors there is an insulating dielectric. This holds the two conductors apart and in an ideal world would not introduce any loss. This dielectric may be solid, but in the case of many low-loss cables it may be semi-air-spaced because it is the dielectric that introduces most of the loss. This may take the form of long 'tubes' of air in the dielectric, or a 'foam' construction where air forms a major part of the material.

Finally, there is a final cover or outer protective sheath. This serves little electrical function, but can prevent earth loops forming. It also gives a vital protection needed to prevent dirt and moisture attacking the cable. However, when burying cable, it is best not to rely on the sheath. Instead use conduit or use special 'bury-direct' cables that are available.

It can be considered that a cable carries current in both the inner and the outer conductors but, because they are equal and opposite, all the fields are confined within the cable and it does not radiate or pick up signals. In reality, the cable operates by propagating an electromagnetic wave inside the cable. As there are no fields outside the cable it is not affected by nearby objects. This means it is ideal for applications where the cable has to be taken through the house and close to many other metallic objects.

As with all feeders, coax has a characteristic impedance. There are two standard values that have been adopted over the years. 75Ω cable is used almost exclusively for domestic TV and VHF FM applications. However, for commercial, amateur and CB applications, 50Ω has been taken as the standard. The reason for the choice of these two standards is largely historical, but arises from the fact that 75Ω coax gives the minimum weight for a given loss, whilst 50Ω coax gives the minimum loss for a given weight. While these two standards are used for the vast majority of coax cable which is produced, it is still possible to obtain other impedances for specialist applications. To obtain these non-standard impedances, it is necessary to approach a specialist supplier and the cost would normally be much higher.

The impedance of coax is chiefly governed by the diameters of the inner and outer conductors. In addition to this, the dielectric constant of the material between the conductors has an influence. The relationship needed to calculate the impedance, Z_0, is given simply by the formula

$$Z_0 = \frac{138}{\varepsilon} \log\left(\frac{D}{d}\right) \text{ , where}$$

D = inner diameter of the outer conductor,

d = diameter of the inner conductor,
ε = dielectric constant of the medium.

When using coax at VHF and UHF it is necessary to ensure that high-quality cable is used. Even comparatively short lengths of poor feeder can introduce levels of loss that can significantly reduce the performance of the whole station. It is wise to be wary of cheap versions of 'RG-58' that are often used for CB applications. Often the braid coverage is less than 50%, resulting in very high levels of loss that might be tolerable below 30MHz but are certainly not at VHF and above. Also beware of computer coaxial cables. These may not have a 50Ω impedance, although those that are often offer high levels of performance.

When choosing coaxial feeder, RG-58 or URM-67 should only be used for short lengths. For longer runs a much lower loss cable will be required. Although this will be expensive it is well worth the additional cost.

Loss is naturally a very important aspect of any feeder. When using coaxial cable, it is of paramount importance to ensure that no moisture enters the feeder. Moisture will pass into the dielectric material that separates the inner and outer conductors, and increase the dielectric loss. It will also cause the braid to oxidise, and reduce the conductivity between the small conductors making up the braid. This will have the effect of increasing heat losses and reducing the effectiveness of the screen. Both of these effects will contribute to the loss. As a result, it is necessary to seal the end of any coax lines and ensure that the outer sheath is intact.

Open wire and twin feeder
Rather than having two concentric conductors to contain the fields associated with a radio frequency signal, it is also possible to use two parallel conductors as in **Fig 2.5**. This type of cable is also known as a ribbon or 'twin' feeder. Sometimes, where the two cables are kept apart at intervals by spacers the feeder is called open-wire feeder, but this is normally only used at frequencies below about 30MHz. This type of feeder works because it does not allow any signal to radiate if the conductors are close together (less than 0.01 wavelengths spacing for most applications) because the fields from both the conductors will be equal and opposite, and hence cancel one another out.

The advantage of this type of cable is that, at lower frequencies, it can be made to have a loss that is much less than coax. However, as the frequency rises and the required spacing falls it does not become a practicable type of feeder and it is not normally used above frequencies of about 150MHz.

The impedance of the feeder can be calculated from the formula

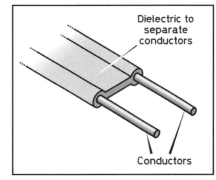

$$Z_0 = \frac{276}{\varepsilon}\log\left(\frac{D}{d}\right) \quad , \text{where}$$

D = distance between the conductors,

Fig 2.5: Twin feeder.

Dielectric to separate conductors

Conductors

d = diameter of the conductors,
ε= dielectric constant of the material between the conductors.

Twin feeder is relatively cheap but, because of its loss at VHF and UHF, it is seldom used at these frequencies. In addition to this it can easily become unbalanced and its performance impaired if it passes close to other objects. It is therefore unsuitable for cable runs within a house. It is worth noting that the translucent variety absorbs moisture and, when this occurs, the loss rises significantly. There are both 75Ω and 300Ω varieties available; the 300Ω variety has a wider spacing and suffers slightly less from absorption. A black plastic variety with 'holes' in the dielectric spacing is far more satisfactory for feeder applications.

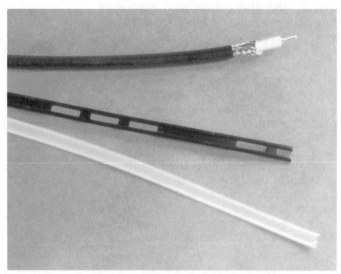

Despite these disadvantages, it can often be used in temporary antenna installations reasonably well. It also finds uses in the construction of several home-made antennas including some vertical installations. Although very convenient, it does not always offer the best electrical performance.

Examples of coaxial cable, black twin and ordinary twin cable.

It is worth noting that an improvised form of twin feeder can be made from ordinary twin lighting flex. The spacing of the two conductors means that it approximates a 75Ω line.

Waveguide

The third type of feeder is known as *waveguide*. It consists of a hollow metal 'pipe'. Usually, it is rectangular as shown in **Fig 2.6** but it possible to have circular waveguide as well. It is different from other forms of feeder in that it does not have conventional conductors as in the case of coax or open-wire feeder. It has an electromagnetic wave travelling *inside* it, the waveguide itself acting as an enclosure along which the wave travels and preventing any energy from escaping.

A signal can be introduced into a waveguide in a number of ways. One is to use a launcher like the one shown in **Fig 2.7**. In this a small probe, which may be the centre conductor of some coax, extends slightly into the waveguide. It is orientated so that it is parallel to the electric field which needs to be

Hollow centre

Conducting outer wall

Fig 2.6: Diagram of a typical waveguide.

set up. Any signal from the coax will then be launched into the waveguide. An alternative method is to use a small loop that encompasses the magnetic lines of force. However the most common method is to use the open-circuit probe.

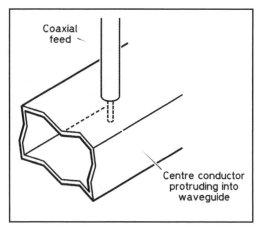

Fig 2.7: An example of a waveguide 'launcher'.

These launchers not only enable signals to be transmitted into the waveguide, but they can also be used to pick signals up as well. Alternatively, the signal can be radiated or picked up directly from the end of the waveguide. In fact an un-terminated waveguide will radiate its signal perfectly well, although its directional properties will not be particularly good for most purposes. In view of this fact, it is very important *never* to look down a waveguide that is connected to a transmitter because it could be radiating energy of a sufficient level to cause damage to the eyes.

A waveguide of particular dimensions cannot operate below a certain frequency, called its *cut-off frequency*. Below this no signals propagate along it. This means that a number of different sizes of waveguide are available dependent upon what frequency or band is in use. These sizes are standardised and allocated numbers in the form WGxx. For instance, a waveguide for use between 2.60GHz and 3.96GHz has internal dimensions of 72 x 34mm and it is given the designation WG10.

The main advantage of waveguide is its low loss at high frequencies when compared with coax. It becomes a viable alternative for some systems above frequencies of 2 - 3GHz. As an example, WG10 made from aluminium has a loss of 0.7dB per 30m. Coax for use at these frequencies would have a very much higher attenuation. Against this, the cost of waveguide is very much higher and as a result it is generally only used in professional applications.

Waveguides are used in a comparatively limited number of instances, and much less in recent years because new varieties of coax have been introduced that operate at much higher frequencies. Their main use is for microwave frequencies in view of their minimum operating frequencies. Waveguides for VHF, or even some UHF frequencies would be too large to make them viable.

BALANCED AND UNBALANCED FEEDERS

Coax and open-wire or twin feeder differ from one another because coax is an *unbalanced* feeder while open-wire or twin feeder is *balanced*. The difference is that an unbalanced feeder has one of the conductors connected to earth. Many antennas including the dipole and Yagi are balanced, having neither element referenced to earth. Antennas such as a ground plane are unbalanced, having one of the connections referenced to earth. For the correct operation, the feeder and the antenna should both be either balanced or unbalanced, or at least appear to be so.

UK designation (RCSC)	EIA designation (Standard US and RG numbers)	Inside dimensions (inches)	Typical external dimensions (inches)	Standard frequency range(GHz)
WG6	WR-650 / RG-69	6.50 x 3.25	6.66 x 3.42	1.12 – 1.70
WG8	WR-430 / RG-104	4.30 x 2.15	4.46 x 2.31	1.70 – 2.60
WG9A	WR-340	3.40 x 1.70	3.56 x 1.86	2.10 x 3.00
WG10	WR-284 / RG-48	2.84 x 1.34	3.00 x 1.50	2.60 – 3.95
WG11A	WR-229	2.29 x 1.145	2.418 x 1.273	3.30 – 4.90
WG12	WR-187 / RG-49	1.872 x 0.872	2.000 x 1.000	3.95 – 5.85
WG13	WR-159	1.590 x 0.795	1.718 x 0.923	4.90 – 7.05
WG14	WR-137 / RG-50	1.372 x 0.622	1.500 x 0.750	5.85 – 8.20
WG15	WR-112 / RG-51	1.122 x 0.497	1.250 x 0.625	7.05 – 10.00
WG16	WR-90 / RG-52	0.900 x 0.400	1.000 x 0.500	8.20 – 12.4
WG17	WR-75	0.750 x 0.375	0.850 x 0.475	10.0 – 15.0
WG18	WR-62 / RG-91	0.622 x 0.311	0.702 x 0.391	12.4 – 18.0

Table 2.1: Standard waveguides with their WG, WR and RG numbers. Note: WR stands for 'Waveguide Rectangular'.

Where a transition between a balanced and unbalanced system takes place, a *balun* is required. The term is derived from the two words **BAL**anced to **UN**balanced.

For example, a coaxial feeder is unbalanced, as it is not symmetrical. The outer braid is generally referenced to earth. Under normal operation of a feeder, the RF current flows on the inside of the outer conductor, and on the outside of the inner conductor. In this way all the RF power is contained within the confines of the feeder. If it is connected to a balanced antenna, such as a dipole, current will result on the outside of the braid. The current flowing on the outside of the cable can result in distortion of the radiation pattern of the antenna; radiation occurs from the braid when transmitting, and it picks up signals when receiving. This can be resolved by the use of a balun.

A number of types of balun can be used. A transformer is probably the most obvious method, but there are several other types that can be used. One is known as a coaxial sleeve balun shown in **Fig 2.8**. Here, the outer sleeve acts as a quarter-wave short-circuit stub and this presents a high impedance to any currents flowing on the outside of the coaxial cable. A Pawsey stub operates in a similar manner (**Fig 2.9**), although the physical implementation is rather different.

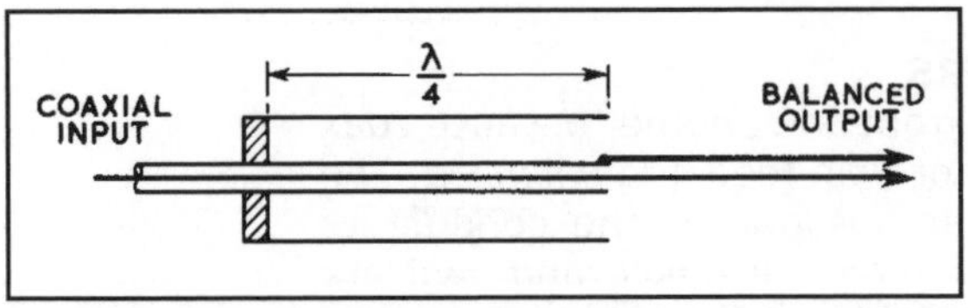

Fig 2.8: A form of coaxial sleeve balun. This acts as a short circuit stub that presents a high impedance to currents flowing on the outside of the cable.

Another method that is often used, especially with thinner cables, is to coil them close to the feed-point of the antenna to act as an RF choke. Typically, about five or six turns are used. When doing this, care must be taken at these frequencies to ensure that the capacitance between the turns on the cable is kept low. If it is too high it will form an LC circuit with its resonant point below the frequency of operation. When this occurs, it will appear as being capacitive and have no effect.

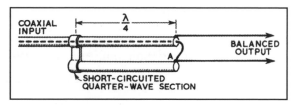

Fig 2.9: The quarter-wave open balun or Pawsey stub.

Ferrite beads are sometimes used. However these should only be used with low powers because they are often lossy and will heat up with any power dissipated in them. This has been known to melt the cable or they may shatter. Accordingly they are really only applicable for low power applications.

IMPEDANCE-MATCHING USING RESONANT LINES

Under certain circumstances, transmission lines can be used as resonant circuits and they can be used to perform impedance-matching transformations. When cut to particular lengths, transmission lines act like high-Q resonant circuits, and they can also be used to act as inductors and capacitors when used away from their resonant points. A musical equivalent to a resonant line is an organ pipe where the resonant properties of the pipe can be used to generate a musical note at the resonant frequency of the pipe that is defined by its length. Often a length of transmission line is far more convenient to use with an antenna than a more traditional lumped-circuit element, and as a result they are often used.

QUARTER-WAVE TRANSFORMER

A quarter-wave length of transmission line can be used to provide an impedance transformation. The input impedance, output impedance and the line impedance of a quarter-wave line are linked by the formula

$$Z_0 = Z_{source} \times Z_{load} .$$

From this, it can be seen that the line impedance is the geometric mean of the source and load impedances. As an example, to match a 100Ω load to a 50Ω line, a quarter-wave length of feeder with an impedance of 70.71Ω should be used. In reality, a length of 75Ω cable is quite satisfactory.

It can be seen from the voltage and current patterns on a quarter-wave transformer that it provides an impedance-inverting property (**Fig 2.10**). Over a quarter wavelength, the voltage and current patterns become reversed.

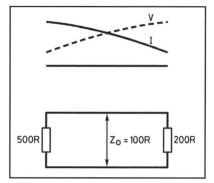

STUB MATCHING

Short sections of transmission line can be used for matching purposes. Those used are generally less than a quarter wavelength and possess a particular value of reactance; they can be used to counteract the effects of unwanted reactance in the antenna

Fig 2.10: The voltage and current waveforms on a quarter-wave matching line showing how the voltage and current waveforms change in magnitude.

system. Dependent upon whether the stub is open-circuit or short-circuit, the transmission line will present either a capacitive or inductive reactance. As before, short lengths of transmission line can often be more convenient to use than lumped or discrete elements, so they are often used.

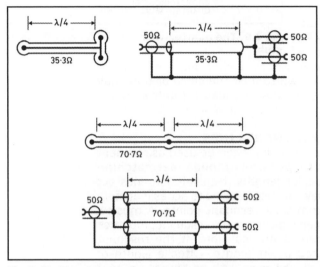

Fig 2.11: Two types of quarter-wave power divider.

POWER DIVIDERS

Quarter-wave transformers can be used to construct power dividers that can be used where two antennas require feeding in parallel. This might happen if two antennas are being stacked or bayed. There are two methods of achieving a power divider as shown in **Fig 2.11**. The first uses a single quarter-wave transformer. This works well if both the loads are well matched in phase and magnitude. The second uses separate quarter-wave transformer sections to feed each antenna. This is more satisfactory because the feeder impedance is 70.7Ω which approximates to the 75Ω feeder that is widely available for television applications. Remember that the velocity factor of the different types of coax cable is different, so a quarter-wavelength is a different physical length - a fact that has caught many people out in the past.

The power divider can be constructed by taking the two lengths of 75Ω coax and connecting them both to the common input. They are coiled in a suitable metal case and connected to the two individual connections as shown in **Fig 2.12**. For low-power applications up to about 50W it is possible to use relatively thin coax such as URM-111. For higher powers thicker coax is required.

COAX CABLE SPECIFICATIONS

Coaxial feeder is by far the most common type of feeder in use. As a result, there is a great variety of different types of coaxial cable that can be bought. In order to standardise these types of cable, type coding specifications are used. Coax is

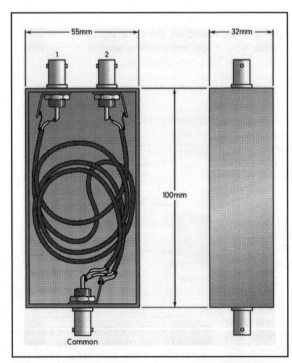

Fig 2.12: A compact two-way power divider suitable for feeding two antennas at 145MHz.

manufactured and sold to these standards. There are two main systems are in use. One originated in the United Kingdom and its type numbers all start with UR. The other system is American with type numbers commencing with the letters RG. As the two systems are different, but cover very similar items, several cables are very similar and alternatives exist between the two systems. A list of the more commonly used cables is shown in **Table 2.2**.
(See coax table over the page)

Although it is possible to go into a local TV or radio shop and buy standard or low-loss coax cable, when using cable for amateur or commercial applications, it is more usual to buy coax with a specific type number. Coax with a type number will have a certain specification. Its dimensions, impedance, loss, velocity factor and so forth will all be defined, even though the manufacturer may not be known.

It is necessary to beware of some of the very cheap types of cable as these may not be fully compliant to the standard and may offer inferior performance. If there is any doubt about the quality of the cable, have a look at the braid. It should cover the dielectric completely. If it does not, it is unlikely to be worth buying. There is a lot of so-called 'RG8' cable available, intended for the cheap end of the CB market. Such cable can often offer very inferior performance and should be avoided. In any case RG8 is an obsolete designation.

CONNECTORS

Of the very wide variety of connectors in use today, some are more familiar than others. Some are used for their high-frequency capability, while others have gained their popularity for their low cost. In any case, it is necessary to know what connectors are available and know about their relative merits and shortcomings.

One of the most widely used VHF/UHF connectors is the standard TV or Belling Lee, shown in **Fig 2.13(a)**. It is almost universally used for domestic television in the United Kingdom because it is very cheap. While it is acceptable for indoor television use, it should not be used for any application where the specification is of importance. It should also not be used out of doors because it is made of aluminium and will corrode quite quickly.

The 'UHF' connector is shown in **Fig 2.13(b)**. Often the plug is referred to as a PL-259 and the socket as an SO-239. It is widely used in amateur radio applications and some video systems. The connectors have a screw fixing to prevent accidental disconnection. The basic connector is designed for use with thick cables, so a reducer has to be used with thinner cables. A 'UHF' connector does not possess a constant impedance, ie its characteristic impedance changes along the length of the connector. This is not a problem in the HF portion of the frequency spectrum but these connectors are only specified for use up to 200MHz, or 500MHz with reduced performance. Ideally, they should not be used above about 100MHz, despite being called 'UHF', and their use is certainly not recommended on the 70cm amateur band. Even at 144MHz, they are not suitable for high power transmitting applications.

Type	Z_0	Outside diameter (mm)	Velocity factor	Attenuation (dB/10m) @100MHz	@1000MHz	Comment
RG-5/U	52.5	8	0.66	1.0	3.8	
RG-6A/U	75	8.4	0.66	1.0	3.7	
RG-9/U	51.0	10.7	0.66	0.66	2.4	
RG-10A/U	50	12.1	0.66	0.66	2.6	
RG-11A/U	75	10.3	0.66	0.76	2.6	
RG-12A/U	75	12.1	0.66	0.76	2.6	
RG-20A/U	50	30.4	0.66	0.22	1.2	
RG-58C/U	50	5.0	0.66	1.8	7.6	
RG-59B/U	75	6.1	0.66	1.2	4.6	
RG-62A/U	93	6.1	0.84	0.9	2.8	
RG-213/U	50	10.3	0.66	0.62	2.6	Polythene dielectric
RG-214/U	50	10.8	0.66	0.76	2.9	Double screened. Silver plated copper wire.
RG-223/U	50	5.5	0.66	1.58	5.4	
UR-43	50	5	0.66	1.3	4.46	
UR-57	75	10.2	0.66	0.63	2.3	Similar to RG-11A/U
UR-67	50	10.3	0.66	0.66	2.52	Similar to RG-213/U
UR-74	51	22.1	0.66	0.33	1.4	
UR76	51	5.0	0.66	1.7	7.3	Similar to RG-58C/U
UR-77	75	22.1	0.66	0.33	1.4	
UR-79	50	21.7	0.96	0.17	0.6	
UR-90	75	6.1	0.66	1.2	4.1	Similar to RG-59B/U
Standard TV Coax *	75	5.1	0.66	1.1	4.0	
Low Loss TV Coax *	75	7.25	0.86	0.75	2.6	Semi-air-spaced

* These cables are not standardised. Figures given are typical only. These figures are given as a guide and there may be some variations.

Table 2.2: Coax cable specifications (typical).

When buying and using UHF connectors, there are several points to note. There are many budget versions of these connectors on the market which have an inferior performance and become quite lossy even at the low end of the VHF portion of the frequency spectrum. Many of these connectors do not have PTFE dielectric supporting the inner conductor and use a brown insulation material instead. When selecting a connector ensure the plating is of a good quality (silver will solder best, although some proprietary plated finishes are just about as good), and there should be two or more solder holes in the body for soldering to the braid. There should be two small tangs on the outer mating edge of the plug, which locate in the serrated ring of the socket and stop the body rotating. If small-diameter cable is to be used, obtain the correct reducer. Often two types are available: one for 75Ω cable, the other for 50Ω cable. The 50Ω reducer is often referred to by the number UG-175 and it is essential to use the correct reducer for the correct cable. It also wise to buy the plugs and reducers together because some manufacturers use different reducer threads.

A BNC connector is shown in **Fig 2.13(c)**. It is widely used professionally, and is found on most oscilloscopes and many other laboratory instruments. It has a bayonet fixing to prevent accidental disconnection while being easy to disconnect when necessary. Electrically, it is designed to present a constant impedance and it is most common in its 50Ω version,

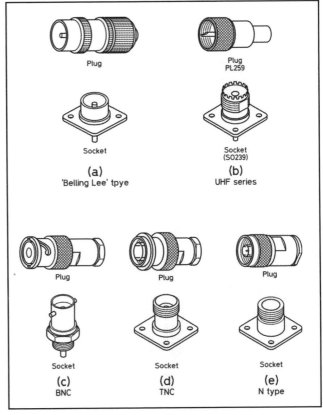

Fig 2.13: Coaxial connectors.

although 75Ω versions can be obtained. Beware not to use connectors with the wrong impedance as this may cause problems later. Top quality BNC connectors can be used at frequencies up to around 3 – 4GHz but, again, beware of inferior products.

The TNC connector shown in **Fig 2.13(d)** is very similar to the BNC connector. The main difference is that it has a screw fitting instead of the bayonet one. In view of the firmer connection resulting from the screw attachment, the performance is slightly better, although their use is not recommended above about 4GHz. With BNC, TNC and N-type connectors, there can be complications. All these connectors are available in 50Ω and 75Ω versions, so it is necessary to ensure the correct impedance type is obtained and used. All of these connectors have evolved over the years and consequently there are several different types. The variations are mostly associated with the cable clamping and centre pin securing method. The original cable clamp type is usually called 'unimproved MIL', the later modification the 'improved', but the best for most uses is the 'pressure sleeve' type. If buying new, opt for the pressure-sleeve type for most applications because it is much easier to fit. However, if it is to be used with some of the double -braided PTFE-dielectric cable such as RG-142, it is easier to use the older clamp types, although the pressure-sleeve type will fit properly with care.

All original clamp types use a free centre pin that is held in place by its solder joint to the inner conductor. Captive contact types have a two-part centre insulator between which fits the shoulder on the centre pin. Improved MIL clamp types may have either free or captive contacts. Pressure sleeve types have a captive centre pin. As an aid to identification, **Fig 2.14** shows these types. Pressure-clamp captive-pin types are easy to spot; they have a ferrule or 'top hat' that assists in terminating the braid,

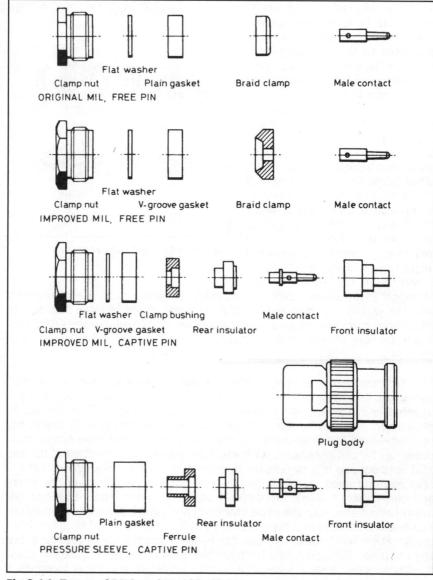

Fig 2.14: Types of BNC and N cable clamps.

a two-piece insulator and a centre pin with a shoulder. Unimproved clamp types have a washer, a plain gasket, a cone-ended braid clamp and a single insulator, often fixing inside the body. Improved types have a washer, a thin ring gasket with a V-groove and usually a conical-braid clamp with more of a shoulder.

FITTING CONNECTORS

One essential element of using coaxial cables is knowing which connectors to use, and the correct fixing of them to the cable. This may appear simple, but it is essential that the connectors are fitted correctly if they are to perform to their specification, and in addition to this they are not always easy to fit. A good summary about their fitting and the pitfalls to be avoided was provided by Roger Blackwell, G4PMK, in May 1988 *RadCom*, and it is still an excellent guide.

When buying connectors, it is important to be able to recognise good and bad types, and know what cables the good ones are for. Using the wrong connector and cable combination is sure to lead to disaster. Any information from sources such as old catalogues is likely to prove useful, especially if it is possible to get the cable cutting dimensions and equivalents lists.

Cables commonly are of one of two families, the American RG (Radio Guide MIL specification) types and the English UR (UniRadio) series. URM-67 is equivalent to RG-213, is 10.5mm diameter and is commonly used with type N and PL-259 connectors. URM-43 (5mm OD) is one usually used with BNC connectors, although these also fit RG-58 cable, since both have simi-lar dimensions.

Tools for the job

To tackle this work successfully, a few special tools make the job much easier. Most of them are normally available in the average amateur radio station, so it is just a matter of sorting through the toolbox. First and foremost is a good soldering iron. Often a small iron may be sufficient unless PL-259s are to be used, when something with a little more heat output is required. Ideally a thermostatically--controlled iron is best. As with most tools, a little extra money spent repays itself handsomely in the future.

A sharp knife is another essential. A Stanley Knife is needed for larger cables, provided that the blade is sharp. For smaller cables, a craft knife or a very sharp penknife can be used. A scalpel will also work well. A word or two of warning is in order, however. Scalpels excel at the job they were designed for cutting flesh. Make sure it is not yours. Use sharp blades, cut away from you, and keep the object you are cutting on the bench, not in your hand. Although sharp, the steel blades are brittle and will shatter if excessive force is applied or they are bent, and bits of sharp blade will shoot all over the place. Dispose of used blades in a box or plastic jar. Model shops have a good range of craft knives which will also do an excellent job.

A pair of sharp, small scissors are needed for cutting braids, and a blunt darning needle (mount it in a handle made from a piece of wood dowelling) is useful for unpicking the braid; so too is a scriber. You will find a small vice a great help as well. For BNC-, TNC- and N-type connectors, some spanners are essential to tighten the gland nuts. The BNC / TNC spanners should be thin 7/16in AF. Those for type N need to be 11/16 x 5/8in AF. BNC spanners are often sold in pairs and are 7/16 x 1/2in AF. Note that the other end is suitable for BNC line sockets. A junior hacksaw is needed to cut larger cables such as URM-67. Finally, for putting heat shrink sleeves over the ends of plugs for outdoor use, some form of heat gun helps, although the shaft of a soldering iron may work. A hot air paint stripper can work well for this job.

Preparing cables

Fitting a plug requires the removal of various bits of outer sheath, braid and dielectric. The important knack to acquire is that of removing one at a time, without damaging what lies underneath. To remove the outer sheath, use a sharp knife or scalpel. Place the knife across the cable and rotate the cable while applying gentle pressure. The object of doing this is to score right round the cable sheath. Now score a line from the ring you just made up to the cable end. If you have cut it just enough, it should be possible to peel away the outer sheath leaving the braid intact underneath. Before trying this on a real piece of cable, practice on a surplus or scrap section first. For some connectors, it is important that this edge of the sheath is a smooth edge at right angles to the cable, so it really is worth getting right.

Braid removal usually just requires a bit of combing out and a pair of scissors. Removal of the dielectric is most difficult with large diameter cables with laid multi-strand inner conductors like URM-67. Again, it is important that the end is a clean, smooth cut at right angles to the cable. This is best achieved by removing the bulk of the dielectric to length. There is a limit to how much dielectric that can be removed at one tie. Between one and two centimetres is about as much as can be attempted without damaging the lay of the inner. For the larger cables, it is best to pare down the bulk of the unwanted material before trying to pull the remainder off the inner. One trick that helps when making up short cables is to fit one plug on the free end before cutting the cable to length. This helps to prevent the inner sliding about when stripping the dielectric.

Fitting PL-259 plugs (without reducer, URM-67 cable)

The first step is to make a clean end. For this large cable, the best way is to use a junior hacksaw. Chopping with cutters or a knife just spoils the whole thing. Having obtained a clean end, refer to **Fig 2.15** for the stripping dimensions. First, remove the sheath braid and dielectric, revealing the length of inner conductor required. Do this by cutting right through the sheath and braid, scoring the dielectric, then removing the dielectric after-wards. Next, carefully remove the sheath back to the dimension indicated, without disturbing the braid. Examine the braid; it should be shiny and smooth. If it has been disturbed or it looks tarnished, start again a little further down. Now the tricky bit. With a hot iron, tin the braid carefully. The idea is to do it with as little solder as possible and often a trace of a non-corrosive flux such as Fluxite helps. Lightly tin the inner conductor also at this stage.

Now slide the coupling piece on to the cable (threaded end towards the free end). [*Do not omit this stage or you will find yourself having to remove the plug after it is fitted.* – Ed.] Examine the plug body. If it is not silver plated, or it looks as if it will not solder easily, apply a file around and through the solder holes. Now screw the body onto the cable, hard. When you've finished, the sheath should have gone into the threaded end of the connector, the inner should be poking out through the hollow pin, and the end of the exposed dielectric should be hard up against the inside shoulder of the plug. Look at the braid through the solder holes. It should not have broken up into a mass of strands; that's why it was tinned. If it has, it is best to start again.

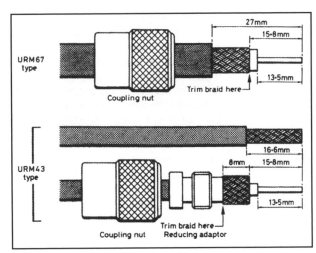

Fig 2.15: PL-259 plug assembly.

If all is well, lightly clamp the cable in the vice. Then apply the soldering iron to the solder holes. Heat it up and apply the solder. It should flow into the holes; if it stays there as a sullen blob, the body isn't hot enough. When you are satisfied with the joint, leave it undisturbed to cool before soldering the inner by heating the pin and feeding solder down inside the pin. Finally, when it is cool, cut any excess protruding inner conductor and file flush with the pin, then screw on the coupling ring. Merely as a confidence check, of course, test for continuity on both inner and outer from one end of the cable to the other, and check that the inner is not shorted to the braid.

Fitting PL-259 plugs (with reducer, URM-43 cable)
First, slide the outer coupler and the reducer on to the cable. Referring to Figure 2.9, remove the outer sheath without nicking the braid. Now, using a blunt needle, gently un-pick the braid a bit at a time until it is all straight and sticking out like a ruff around the cable.

Remove the dielectric, without nicking the inner conductor to leave the specified amount of dielec-tric. Tin the inner conductor. Bring up the reducer until the end of the reducer is flush with the end of the outer sheath. Fold the braid back so it lies evenly over the shank of the reducer, then cut off the excess braid with scissors so that it is not in danger of getting trapped in the threads. Smooth it down once more, then offer up the plug body and, while holding the reducer and cable still, screw on the plug body until it is fully home. The only really good way of doing this is with two pairs of pliers. Now hold the assembly in the vice and ready the soldering iron. There has been a spirited discussion from time to time about the advisability of soldering the braid through the holes; the best information is that it should be soldered. If it is not soldered, the cable will ultimately fail. So with a big iron, solder the braid through the holes.

See the section above for advice. Finally, solder and trim the inner conductor and test the assembly as described ear-lier.

Fitting BNC and N plugs

Both BNC and N-type connectors are termed 'constant impedance connectors'. When correctly assembled, the system impedance of 50Ω is maintained right through the connector. For this to be true it is vital that the cable fits the connector correctly. Therefore, check that each part fits the cable properly after it has been prepared. Refer to **Fig 2.16** for BNC dimensions and **Fig 2.17** for N-types.

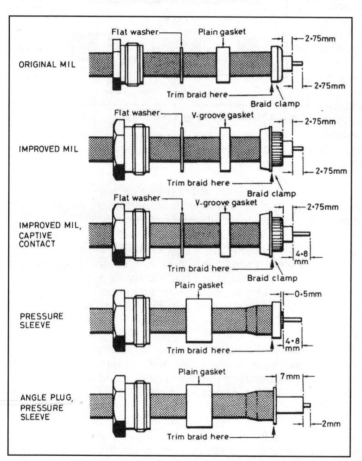

Fig 2.16: BNC dimensions – plugs and in-line sockets.

Original or unmodified clamp types

Slide the nut, washer and gasket on the cable in that order. With a sharp knife, score through the outer sheath by holding the knife and rotating the cable, without nicking the braid. Run the knife along the cable from the score to the end, then peel off the outer sheath. Using a blunt needle or other suitable instrument, start to un-pick the braid enough to enable the correct length of dielectric to be removed. Now slip the braid clamp on, pushing it firmly down to the end of the outer sheath. Finish un-picking the braid, comb it smooth, then trim it with scissors so that it just comes back to the end of the conical section of the clamp. Be sure that the braid wires aren't twisted. Now fit the inner pin and make sure that the open end of the pin will fit up against the dielectric. Take the pin off and lightly tin the exposed inner conductor. Refit the pin and solder it in place by placing the soldering iron bit (tinned but with the solder wiped off) on the side of the pin opposite the solder hole. Feed a small quantity of solder (22SWG or so works best) into the hole. Allow to cool and examine. If this has been done carefully, the dielectric should not have melted. Usually it does, and swells up, so with the sharp knife trim it back to size. This is essential as otherwise the plug will not assemble properly. Remove any excess solder from around the pin with a fine file. Now push the gasket and washer up against the clamp nut, check the braid dressing on the clamp, then push the assembly into the plug body. Gently firm home the gasket with a small screwdriver or rod and then start the clamp nut by hand. Tighten the clamp nut by a spanner, using a second spanner to hold the plug body still; it must not rotate. Finally, check the completed job with an ohm-meter.

Modified or improved clamp types
In general this is similar to the technique for unmodified clamp types described above. There are some important differences, however. The gasket has a V-shaped groove in it, which must face the cable clamp. The clamp has a corresponding V-shaped profile on one side. The other side may be conical or straight sided, depending on the manufacturer. If the clamp end has straight sides, then the braid is fanned out and cut to the edge of the clamp only, not pushed down the sides. Some types have a small PTFE insulator which is fitted before the pin is put on (common on plugs for the small RG-174 cable). This shows why having the assembly instructions for the particular type of plug is a good idea. Still, by using these instructions as a guide, it shouldn't be too difficult to get it right, even if it does not fit the first time. One important point - if the plug has been assembled correctly and tightened up properly, the clamp will have (intentionally) cut the gasket. It is then rather difficult

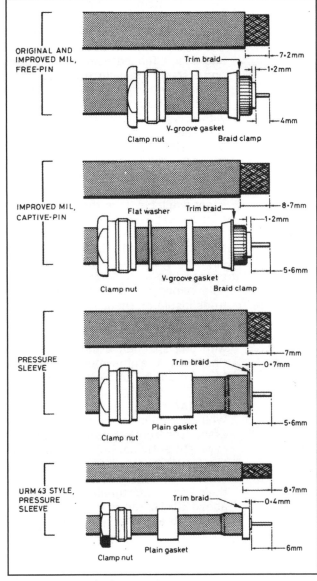

Fig 2.17: N-type dimensions – plugs, angle plugs and in-line sockets.

to re-use it because the gasket, being thin, will not stand a second attempt. The thicker gasket types will often allow careful re-use.

Captive-contact types
These have a small shoulder on the pin, and a rear insu-lator which fits between the pin and the cable. Most types use a thick gasket and a ferrule, although some use a V-grooved braid clamp and thin gasket. I shall describe the ferrule type, as this is the most common, and the easier of the two to fit.

First, slip the nut and gasket on to the cable. Refer to Figs 2.16 or 2.17 for cutting dimensions, then strip off the correct amount of outer sheath by rotating the cable, producing a neat scored circle. Score back to the end of the cable and peel off the unwanted sheath. Comb out the braid, and with it fanned out evenly around the cable, slide the ferrule (small end first) on the dielectric-covered inner conductor. Push it home so that the narrow portion of the ferrule slides under the outer sheath, and the end of the outer sheath rests against the ferrule shoulder. Trim the braid with scissors to the edge of the ferrule. Slide up the gasket so that it rests gently against the ferrule shoulder, which will prevent the braid from being disturbed. Using the sharp knife, trim the dielectric back to the indicated dimension, without nicking the inner conductor. Fit the rear insulator, which will have a recess on one side to accommodate the protruding di-electric. Incidentally, if the right size for the particular plug is not available, trim the dielectric until if fits; but do not overdo it. Now trim the exposed inner conductor to length and check by fitting the pin, whose shoulder should rest on the rear insulator unless the inner has been cut too long. Tin the inner lightly, then fit the pin and solder it by applying the iron tip (cleaned of excess solder) to the side of the pin opposite from the solder hole and feed a small amount of solder into the hole. Allow to cool, and remove excess solder with a fine file. Now fit the front insulator (usually separate from the body) and push the whole assembly into the body. Push down the gasket gently into the plug body with a small rod or screwdriver. Start the nut by hand, then tighten fully with one spanner, using the other to prevent the body from rotating. Check with the ohm-meter and then start on the other end, remembering to put the nut and gasket on first.

SUMMARY

While the main focus is always on the antenna itself, the feeder and its associated connectors are equally important. It is possible to have an excellent antenna, but not to capitalise on its performance by neglecting the feeder and its connectors. It is only possible to have an optimum antenna system if all the elements contained within it are operating at their best. Unfortunately, the cost of feeder, especially for frequencies above 30MHz can represent a significant investment, but this will enable the whole antenna system to operate correctly.

REFERENCES AND FURTHER READING

[1]   *International Microwave Handbook*, Andy Barter, G8ATD, (RSGB).
[2]   *The VHF/UHF Handbook*, edited Andy Barter, G8ATD (RSGB).

In this Chapter

- BASIC DIPOLE
- FOLDED DIPOLE
- LENGTH
- QUICK AND EASY DIPOLE
- 50MHz DIPOLE
- CROSSED DIPOLES
- HORIZONTALLY-POLARISED OMNI-V
- HALO
- MINI-HALO
- WIDE-BAND 23cm BEAM

The dipole is probably the most important type of antenna. Although it is not commonly used at VHF and UHF on its own, it is very widely used as the basic element in many other types of antenna. For example it is used as the driven element in the Yagi. Despite this, even in its basic form, a dipole can provide quite satisfactory service, providing the solution to a number of antenna requirements. It is simple and easy to construct, and where gain or directivity is not particularly important it can often be an ideal solution.

BASIC DIPOLE

A dipole is a simple device that contains two 'poles' or terminals into which radiating currents flow. Being more specific, a dipole is generally taken to be an antenna comprising a resonant length of wire cut to enable it to be connected to the feeder, as shown in **Fig 3.1**. For VHF and UHF applications a dipole that is a half-wavelength long is most common, but any multiple of half-wavelengths can be used.

The current distribution along a dipole is sinusoidal, falling to zero at the end but rising to its maximum in the middle. Conversely, the voltage is low at the middle and rises to a maximum at the ends as shown in **Fig 3.2**.

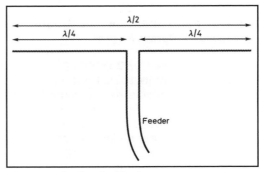

Fig 3.1: The basic dipole.

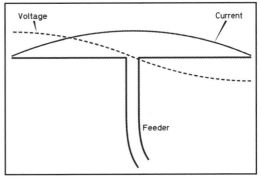

Fig 3.2: Current and voltage on a dipole.

The feed impedance is also very important. For the half-wave version, the antenna is fed in the centre. Here, the current is high and the voltage is low. From Ohm's Law it is possible to deduce that the impedance is low. In fact, the impedance of a dipole in free space is 73.13Ω, making it ideal to feed with 75Ω coax. A dipole that is a multiple of half-wavelengths can be fed anywhere that the current reaches a maximum and where the voltage falls to a minimum.

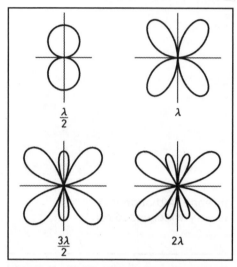

Fig 3.3: Polar diagrams of dipole antennas of different lengths.

The feed impedance of the dipole can be changed by the proximity of other objects. Naturally, the ground has an effect, particularly when the antenna is low. However, for most VHF and UHF applications the antenna is likely to be mounted several wavelengths away from the ground. Instead, other nearby objects are more likely to have effects. If the dipole is one element of a larger antenna, the other elements will have a significant effect on the feed impedance, sometimes reducing it to a small value.

The polar diagram is shown in **Fig 3.3(a)**. From this it can be seen that the direction of maximum sensitivity or radiation is at right angles to the axis of the antenna. It then falls to zero along the axis. However, if the length of the antenna is changed then this pattern is altered. As the length is extended the main lobes move progressively towards the axis of the antenna.

FOLDED DIPOLE

In its basic form a dipole consists of a single wire or conductor cut in the middle to accommodate the feeder. It has already been seen that the feed impedance can be altered by the proximity of other objects. This can cause problems with matching and because resistance losses in the antenna system can start to become significant.

In addition to this, many antennas have to be able to operate over larger bandwidths than the basic dipole can cover. This can happen when trying to design an antenna that has to cover a complete amateur band. A greater problem in terms of bandwidth is encountered with antennas for the VHF FM broadcast band that stretches from 88 to 108MHz.

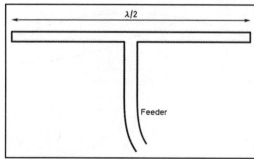

Fig 3.4: The basic folded dipole.

Fortunately it is possible to overcome both of these problems, at least in part, by using a 'folded dipole'. Essentially a folded dipole is formed by taking a standard dipole and then adding a further conductor from one end to the other as shown in **Fig 3.4**. If the conductors of the basic dipole and the added section are of the same diameter, the impedance of the antenna is raised by a factor of four. By changing the ratio of the diameters of the two conductors the impedance can be changed. This means that it is possible to obtain an almost exact match for most requirements. However, for most applications where the conductor diameter is constant, the impedance of a folded dipole is taken to be 300Ω.

LENGTH

The length of a dipole is quite critical because the antenna is a resonant circuit. However, its length is not exactly the same as a half-wavelength (or multiple of a half-wavelength) in free space. There are several reasons for this, and it means that an antenna will be slightly shorter than the length calculated for a wave travelling in free space.

For a half-wave dipole, the free-space wavelength is calculated and this is multiplied by a factor A. For VHF and UHF antennas, A is generally about 0.96. It is mainly dependent upon the ratio of the length of the antenna to the thickness of the wire or tube. A graph showing this relationship is given in **Fig 3.5**.

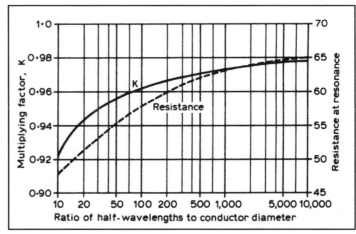

Fig 3.5: Graph of length factor against length / diameter ratio.

In order to calculate the length of a half-wave dipole, one of the simple formulae given below can be used.

$$Length\ (m) = \frac{150 \times A}{f\ (MHz)}\ ,\ or\ Length\ (in) = \frac{5905 \times A}{f\ (MHz)}\ .$$

Even though calculated lengths are normally quite repeatable, it is always best to make any prototype antenna slightly longer than the calculations might indicate. This needs to be done because factors, such as changes in the thickness of wire being used, may alter the length slightly and if it is slightly too long it can be trimmed until it resonates on the right frequency. It is best to trim the antenna length in small steps because the wire or tube cannot be replaced very easily once it has been removed.

QUICK AND EASY DIPOLE

The construction of a basic dipole is very easy. Most of the details will depend upon its use, where it is to be placed and the materials available for its construction. It may be made simply from ordinary wire or tubing. The overall length must be determined (as shown above) and then, having cut this length it must be split in the middle for the feeder, one conductor from each leg of the antenna being connected to each conductor in the feeder.

As the maximum voltage points of the antenna are at the free ends, care should be taken to ensure that they are kept away from nearby conductive objects. This is because the antenna may be de-tuned by them, which can drastically reduce the signal at the receiver. However, the centre of the dipole is far less sensitive.

One very simple way of making a dipole, complete with feeder for low-power experimental or temporary use is with some low-current mains flex. When used as a feeder for radio frequency signals, this type of wire is a reasonably close approximation to 75Ω twin or open-wire feeder. Another alternative to this is speaker wire.

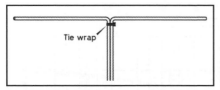

Fig 3.6: A simple method of making a temporary dipole.

To make up the dipole, the two insulated wires should be split back away from one another and opened out as shown in **Fig 3.6**. The centre should then be secured to prevent the cable opening out any further, for instance by using a cable tie such as those available from most electronics component or DIY stockists. The length of wire that has not been split can then be used as the feeder.

This type of antenna would not normally be used for a permanent installation, but can be very useful as a temporary measure, especially when performing experiments. It has the advantage that it can be constructed in a very few minutes and from cable that is likely to be available around the shack.

50MHz DIPOLE

A dipole can be easily constructed for use on the 50MHz band. As antenna sizes for this band are larger than those for the higher frequency bands, multi-element arrays may not be suitable for all locations and a dipole has to suffice. Despite this, it is still possible to make many DX contacts with this type of antenna.

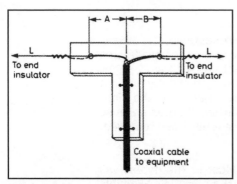

Fig 3.7: The centre connections for the 50MHz dipole. Accurate measurement is needed and the two dipole legs L must be 2.8m. This length includes A or B which are the distances between the ends of the coax and the dipole wires.

Construction is straightforward, and the centre is shown in **Fig 3.7** The short distance between the coaxial cable and the connecting points of the antenna wire itself must be included as part of the antenna length. To make the antenna resonant at 51MHz, the centre of the band, the dipole has a length of 2.8 metres, each leg of the antenna being half this value.

If the antenna is to be used for low-power applications, an effective balun can be made using ferrite beads slipped over the feeder about 30 to 40mm away from the antenna. Beads, part number FB-BLN FB-73 2401 (available from Ferromagnetics, PO Box 577, Mold, Clwyd CH7 1AH) are suitable for slipping over RG-58AU, UR-43, UR-76 or any cable with an outside diameter of 5mm. Six beads suffice and they take up a length of 28mm. They should obviously

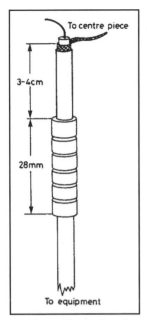

Fig 3.8: The balun for the 50MHz dipole is made from six beads that can be slipped over the coaxial cable.

be slipped into place before the coax is connected to the dipole legs, and they can be held in place by tape. If the antenna is to be used outside, this tape should be weatherproof, eg self-amalgamating tape (see **Fig 3.8**).

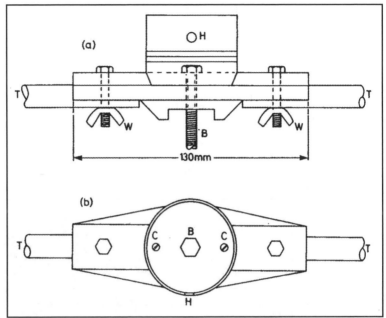

Fig 3.9: The centre piece used for constructing a rotatable dipole.

50MHz ROTATABLE DIPOLE

A wire dipole is obviously not suitable for rotation, and there are instances where it is advantageous to be able to orientate the dipole to obtain the best results. Construction of a rotatable dipole is best achieved by using a commercially-available dipole centre piece of the type that accommodates elements made of aluminium tube as shown in **Fig 3.9**. These centre pieces are manufactured to fix to either square or round masts or booms and have a waterproof area where the coax can be connected to the elements.

Construction of the antenna is again very straightforward. The dipole legs can be made from 13mm diameter tubing. The overall length of the dipole should again include the length of the coax interconnection and, as a result, each leg of the dipole should be cut to 1.38m. The distance between the tube ends and the coaxial cable is approximately 20mm, giving the correct total length for the dipole to be resonant at 51MHz. Holes need to be drilled in the end of each element to enable them to be fitted and secured in the centre-piece using the bolts and wing nuts, W, on the diagram. The bolt, B, is used to fix the assembly to the mast or boom in the case of a more complicated antenna. Connections to the dipole legs are made using the fixings labelled C. Again, ferrite beads can be used to provide the balun.

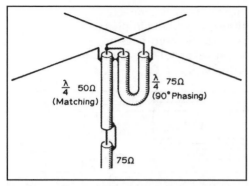

Fig 3.10: The arrangement for a crossed-dipole antenna.

An antenna for 435MHz can be made using the same form of construction. Each dipole leg will need to be 144mm to give the correct overall length. For the balun, only four beads are needed to provide sufficient level of inductance.

CROSSED DIPOLES

This antenna is also known by the name 'turnstile', as this aptly describes its appearance (**Fig 3.10**). It provides a simple, yet effective horizontally-polarised antenna suitable for base station use. It consists of two horizontal dipoles mounted at right angles to one another and fed with an equal amount of power, but with a 90° phase difference. The antenna provides a very good match to 75Ω coax and is acceptable with 50Ω feeder. It can be

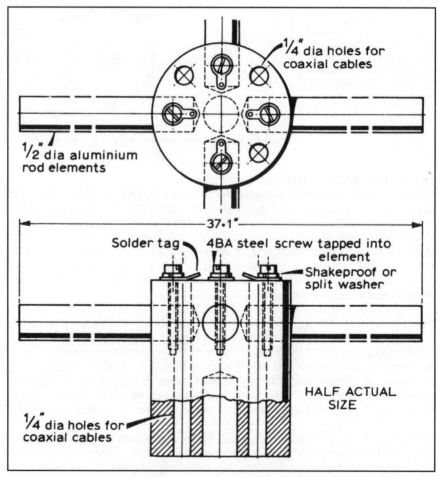

Fig 3.11: Details of the centre insulator for the crossed-dipole antenna.

trimmed to obtain a satisfactory level of VSWR. The radiation pattern is almost omnidirectional.

To provide mechanical rigidity, construction similar to that shown in **Fig 3.11** and **Fig 3.12** can be used. This provides a convenient arrangement for mechanically fixing the antenna elements and for enabling all the required connections to be made. The antenna once found use as a horizontally-polarised omnidirectional antenna for mobile applications. However, it exhibited a large wind resistance but, more importantly, the dipole elements were often around eye height and proved dangerous. For base-station applications, it is still a useful antenna, although it does not offer any gain when compared to a dipole. However its omnidirectional radiation pattern in the horizontal plane makes it useful when a rotatable antenna is not required.

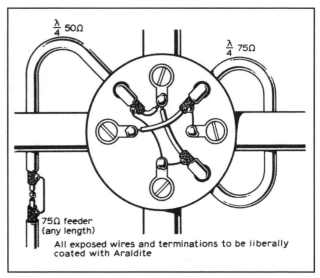

Fig 3.12: Details of the connections for the coaxial sections of the crossed dipole antenna.

Horizontally-polarised Omni-V

This can be conveniently used as a base station antenna where either a bi-directional or near omnidirectional radiation pattern is required (**Figs 3.13** and **3.14** *see over page*). The antenna consists of a pair of half-wave dipoles mounted one above the other, and fed using an interesting arrangement with a quarter-wave short-circuited stub. Two Q-bars are tapped down the stubs to a point where the impedance is 600Ω. As the two antennas are fed in parallel, this gives an overall impedance of 300Ω. A 4:1 balanced-to-unbalanced transformer is used to enable the antenna to be fed with 75Ω coax. For 50Ω coax, the Q-bars can be repositioned by equal amounts on both stubs while monitoring the VSWR.

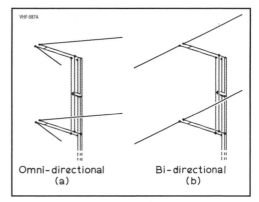

Fig 3.13: Basic concept of the Omni-V antenna in both its omnidirectional and bi-directional configurations.

The antenna provides gain over a single dipole as it is essentially a pair of stacked dipoles. Even in its omnidirectional version it still provides some gain.

Halo

The halo was widely used for mobile applications some years ago, and is still used on some occasions today. Obtaining its name as a result of its shape, it is an almost omnidirectional antenna that gives a horizontally-

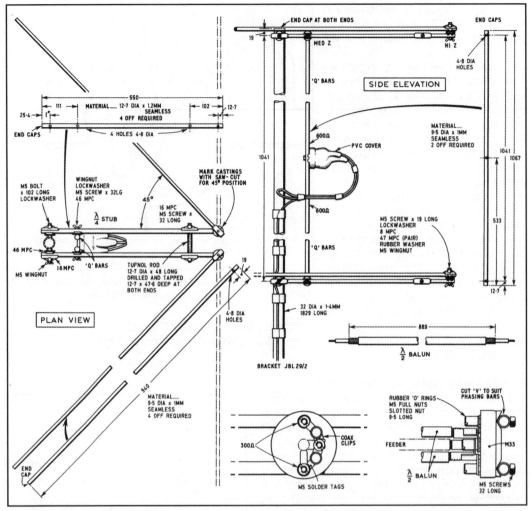

Fig 3.14: Mechanical construction details of the Omni-V antenna (dimensions in mm).

polarised signal. It is essentially a half-wave dipole that is bent into a circle or sometimes a square. A null in its radiation pattern is seen in the direction of the gap between the two ends. When used for mobile applications it should be at least 0.35λ above the vehicle metalwork to operate satisfactorily.

A typical halo can be made like that shown in **Fig 3.15**. The circumference of the antenna element itself is a half wavelength, and there should be a gap of about 30mm between the two ends of the wires or tubes used for the elements. Matching is provided using a gamma-match as shown in the diagram.

Mini-Halo

For some applications, a full-sized 2m halo may be too large, and it is possible to construct a smaller mini-halo. This interesting design has an

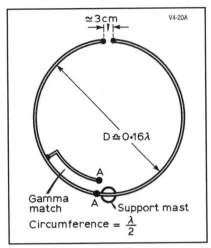

Fig 3.15: Construction of a halo antenna.

the main brass tubing of the antenna itself, the gamma-matching section, and the capacitor assembly. Of these, the capacitor section is the most critical and must be constructed with care. To allow a sufficient number of threads to be cut in the wall of the outer sleeve a 6BA tap (or equivalent metric) is used. It should be noted that the inner of the two tube sections making up the capacitor is secured to one end of the circular element by a screw that force-fits into the bore of the tube. The polythene or PTFE lining of this inner tube is fitted to the other end of the circular element by cutting a thread on its outer diameter and force-screwing the lining over this thread. To assemble, the outer sleeve of the capacitor is slipped over the inner sleeve, the PTFE end of the element sprung away from the sleeve end and then inserted into the bore of the capacitor inner sleeve. More details are shown in **Fig 3.17** and **Fig 3.18** *see over page.*

The gamma match is of the same dimensions as for a full-sized halo,

external diameter of only 150mm (6in) and this makes it ideal for many applications where size is an problem.

The overall design is shown in **Fig 3.16**. There are three main sections:

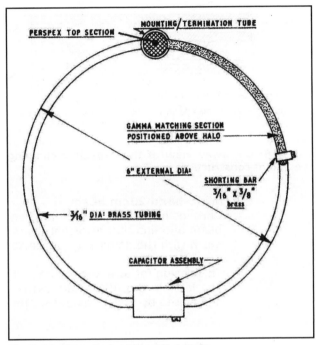

Fig 3.16: Top view of the Mini-Halo.

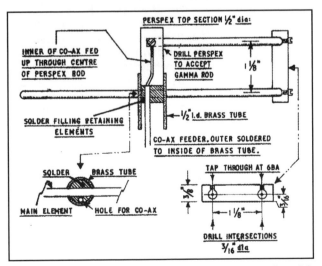

Fig 3.17: Side elevation of the completed halo with drilling details for the gamma-match support and Perspex mounting rod.

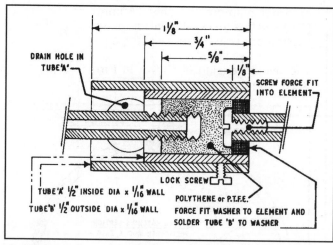

Fig 3.18: Cut-away view of the capacitor showing the method of construction.

and should be approximately 110mm long. In setting up the system, the outer sleeve of the capacitor is used to bring the antenna to resonance and then, in conjunction with a VSWR bridge, the gamma match is set for a minimum level of reflected power.

Its small size would imply a narrow bandwidth, but this antenna can operate satisfactorily over the whole 2m band.

Wide-band 23cm beam

Curtains of phased dipoles have been used for many years to provide a beam antenna, but in recent years this approach has not been used as much with the dominance of the Yagi beam antenna.

This design for a wide-band beam by F5JIO appeared in *Radio-REF* 1/97 and later in the RSGB *RadCom* feature 'Eurotek' which was translated and edited by Erwin David, G4LQI.

In the development of the antenna F5JIO consulted *Rothammel*, the German antenna bible which gives the following guidelines for the reflector plane:

- For the best F/B ratio, the reflector should extend at least half a wavelength beyond the perimeter of the curtain on all sides.
- If made of wire or mesh instead of solid sheet metal to reduce windage, the wire pitch should be λ or less.
- A reflector plane spaced $^5/_8\lambda$ behind the radiator adds a maximum gain of up to 7dB, but a spacing of 0.1 to 0.3λ provides a better F/B ratio.
- If spaced at least 0.3λ behind the curtain, the reflector plane does not affect the feed-point impedance of the array.

Details for the matching of the antenna can be seen in the diagram. With the antenna dimensions given in **Fig 3.19**, the feed-point impedance of each dipole pair is approximately 600Ω balanced. There are three pairs in parallel which divides this impedance by three to give 200Ω, and a 4:1 re-entrant balun transforms this to provide an excellent match to 50Ω coax which is unbalanced. Note that as each dipole is supported at its voltage node, the insulators need to be of good quality.

The construction of the antenna is fairly straightforward, although reasonable care and precision are required. Being a 23cm band antenna, it is quite small and therefore windage is not normally a problem and this

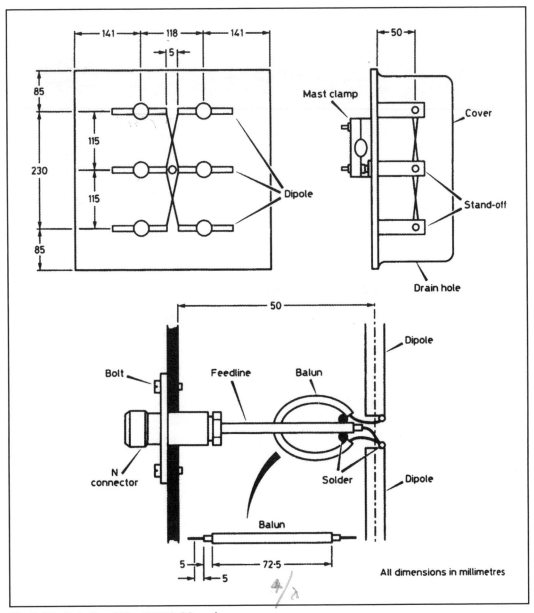

Fig 3.19: Details of the F5JIO 23cm beam.

makes a solid reflector feasible. This then means that the plate used as the reflector can be used as the support for the other components. During construction it is necessary to bend the phasing rods slightly so that they do not touch at the cross-over points. Then, for weather protection, a plastic food container can used as a radome. This can be used as the RF absorption appears to be negligible and it is much cheaper than a Teflon equivalent.

Parts list (Dimensions in mm)

Reflector	400 x 400 (340 min) 2.5 mm thick aluminium sheet (Qty 1)
Stand-offs	Teflon (or PVC) 60L x 20D (Qty 6)
Dipoles:	Brass, silvered, 108L x 6D (Qty 6)
Phasing rods	Wire, silvered 2D (Qty 4)
Connector	N-type (Qty1)
Feed-line	Semi-rigid coax 50Ω approx 4D (Qty 1)
Balun	as 06 above 92.5L (Qty 1)
Bolt	M3 x 8 SS (Qty 4)
Cover	Plastic food container (Qty 1)
Mast clamp	From TV antenna (Qty 1)

Table 3.1: F5JIO 23cm dipole array with reflector plane. Use in conjunction with Fig 3.19.

REFERENCES AND FURTHER READING

[1]   *Radio Communication Handbook* 9th Edition, Edited by Mike Dennison, G3XDV, and John Fielding, ZS5JF (RSGB).

[2]   *VHF/UHF Handbook*, Edited by Andy Barter, G8ATD (RSGB).

Chapter 4
The Yagi

In this Chapter
- THE DESIGN
- GAIN
- FEED IMPEDANCE
- STACKING YAGIS
- PA3HBB / G0BZF PORTABLE 3-ELEMENT 6m YAGI
- G3ROO FIVE-ELEMENT 70cm YAGI

The Yagi is undoubtedly the most common form of 'beam' or directive antenna in use today. It is widely used for amateur applications, but it is even more extensively used in the domestic arena because virtually all TV antennas (with the exception of some of the small set-top loops and satellite antennas) are Yagis. On top of this, the Yagi is also used extensively in the commercial world. It is very effective while being relatively easy to construct, and sturdy enough to withstand the rigours of the weather. Naturally, there is an excellent variety of commercially-manufactured Yagi antennas available for all applications from amateur radio to domestic radio and television, as well as commercial applications. However, it is still interesting and rewarding for the radio amateur to build a Yagi, especially as it can then be tailored exactly to his / her requirements.

The name of the antenna may seem rather unusual. The full name for it is the Yagi-Uda, derived from the names of its two Japanese inventors, Professor Yagi and his student Uda. The antenna was first outlined in a paper that Yagi himself presented in 1928. Since then its use has grown rapidly to the stage where today a television antenna is synonymous with one having a central boom with lots of elements attached.

THE DESIGN
The Yagi has a dipole as its fundamental component. To this, further 'parasitic' elements are added. They are called parasitic because they are not directly connected to the coax feeder. Instead they operate by picking up power from the dipole and then using it to affect the properties of the whole antenna.

The amplitude and phase of the current induced in these elements is dependent upon their length, and the spacing between them and the dipole or driven element. The phase of the signals from the driven element and a parasitic element can be adjusted so that they cancel one another out in one direction and reinforce one another in another direction. This concentrates the power being radiated from the antenna in one direction.

It is not possible to have complete control over both the amplitude and phase of the currents in all of the parasitic elements. This means that complete cancellation in one direction cannot be achieved. Nevertheless it is still possible to obtain a high degree of reinforcement in one direction and have a high level of gain, and also have a high degree of cancellation in another to provide a good F/B ratio.

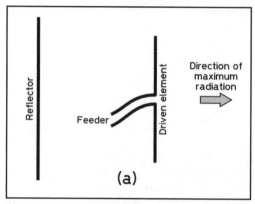

Fig 4.1a

To obtain the required phase shift, an element can be made either inductive or capacitive. If the parasitic element is made *inductive*, ie longer than the driven element, the induced currents are in such a phase that they *reflect* the power away from the parasitic element. This causes the antenna to radiate more power in the direction from the longer parasitic element to the driven element. An element that does this is called a *reflector*. It can be made inductive by tuning it below resonance. Generally it is made about 5% *longer* than the driven element. The reflector is added to the antenna as shown in **Fig 4.1(a)**.

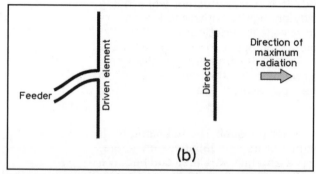

Fig 4.1: Parasitic elements enable the power from the antenna to be concentrated in a particular direction. In (a) the parasitic element acts as a reflector, while in (b) the parasitic element acts as a director.

If the parasitic element is made *capacitive*, the induced currents are in such a phase that they direct the power radiated by the whole antenna in the direction from the driven element to the parasitic element. An element which does this is called a *director*. It can be made capacitive by making the it about 5% *shorter* than the driven element. A director is added to the antenna as shown in **Fig 4.1(b)**.

In order to increase the effect of beaming the power in a certain direction further directors can be added. However, additional reflectors have little noticeable effect so, normally, only one reflector is used. A typical example of a Yagi using a reflector and several directors is shown in **Fig 4.2**.

GAIN

The gain of a Yagi depends primarily upon the number of elements it has. However, the spacing between the elements also has an effect. As the overall

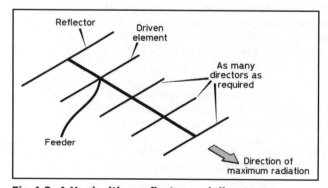

Fig 4.2: A Yagi with a reflector and directors.

performance has so many inter-related variables, many early designs were not able to realise the full performance. Today, computer programmes are able to optimise designs and, as a result, the performance of antennas has been improved.

The gain will obviously vary slightly from one antenna to another dependent upon a number of factors. As a broad guide, a two-element design will give a maximum of around 5dB gain over a dipole. A three-element design will provide a total gain of around 7dBd. Additional directors will give further gain, the actual amount will depend upon how many directors are used. Obviously, the more directors the greater the gain, but the amount of gain an additional director will give depends upon how many are there already. If there are only a few, an extra one will give more gain than if there are many. A four-element antenna will have a gain of up to about 9dBd so the second director has added about 2dB gain, but as a rule of thumb each director will add just under 1dB. For example an 11-element array has a maximum gain of about 13.5dBd and a 12-element array has a gain of just under 14.5dBd (see **Fig 4.3**). This is only true if the antenna is operating under ideal conditions. There are many reasons why antennas operate at much less than their optimum values of gain. For instance, the design may not have been fully optimised, the antenna may be de-tuned by nearby objects, the match between the feeder and the antenna may not be optimum.

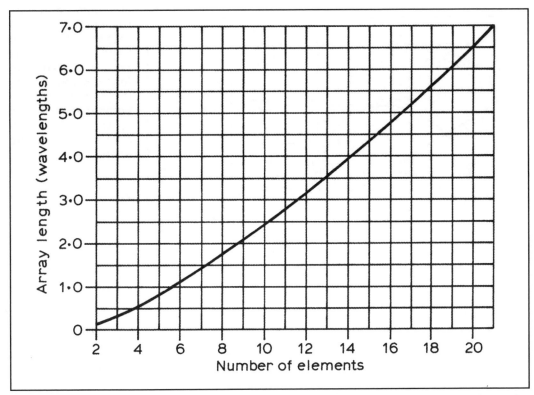

Fig 4.3: Optimum gain in decibels of a Yagi antenna over a dipole (reproduced from *The ARRL Antenna Book*, with permission).

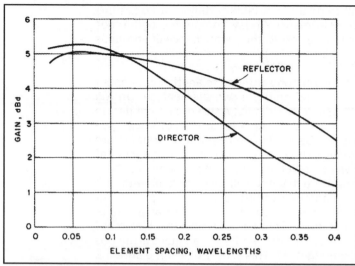

Fig 4.4: A plot of the maximum level of gain achievable from a two-element Yagi as the element spacing is altered (reproduced from *The ARRL Antenna Book*, with permission).

Looking at a two-element design more closely, the maximum gain is achieved when the spacing is very close. Surprisingly, an antenna with a single director gives more gain than one with a reflector for very close values of element spacing (**Fig 4.4**). As the spacing between the driven element and parasitic element is increased a reflector gives a higher level of gain.

The fact that a Yagi has gain means that it needs orientating in the required direction, probably using a motor-controlled rotator. When considering the use of a directional antenna, the cost of such a rotator should be kept in mind. It should also be remembered that as the gain of the antenna is increased so the beam-width decreases and the orientation becomes more critical.

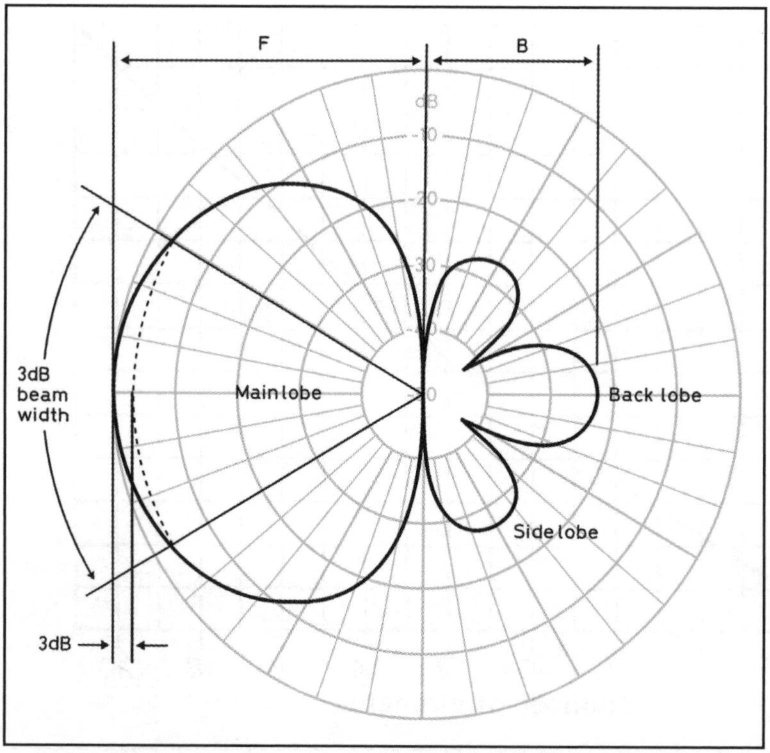

When looking at the gain of the antenna, it is also necessary to consider the F/B ratio. It can be seen from the typical Yagi polar diagram shown in **Fig 4.5** there is a significant lobe from the back of the antenna. It is not possible to obtain a null here because the Yagi uses parasitic elements. If it had two 'driven elements'

Fig 4.5: Polar diagram of a typical Yagi, showing the F/B ratio and 3dB beam-width.

there would be complete control of phasing and amplitude. Even so, it should be possible to obtain a F/B ratio of at least 10dB even when low values of gain are used. However, it should be noted that the points of maximum forward gain and maximum F/B ratio do not coincide. If an antenna is adjusted for maximum gain, it does not produce the best F/B ratio. Similarly when adjusted for maximum F/B ratio there is a small penalty in terms of forward gain.

FEED IMPEDANCE

Apart from altering the gain, the element spacing alters the feed impedance of the antenna. In fact it has a far greater effect on this than the gain for most instances. By altering the spacing, it is possible to ensure that a good match is achieved between the feeder and the antenna itself.

For a two-element Yagi consisting of a driven element plus a reflector, the feed impedance is about 50Ω if the spacing is just over 0.2λ. A 75Ω match is achieved for a spacing of just under 0.3λ. Below a spacing of 0.2λ, the impedance falls away rapidly and it can drop to 5Ω or less for a spacing of 0.1λ. The resistance peaks at around 90Ω for about 0.5λ spacing. The addition of further elements complicates the issue considerably but, generally, the impedance is reduced. In any case a certain amount of experimentation is needed to perfect the design.

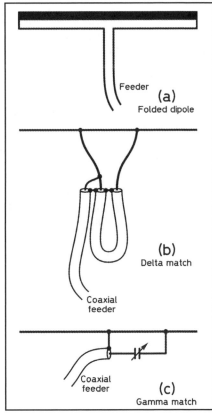

Matching the antenna to the feeder is important. As most feeders used in amateur applications standardise on 50Ω, it is necessary to provide a means of matching the driven element to the feeder. A variety of methods can be used. The easiest is to adjust the inter-element spacing and parasitic element lengths to provide a good match. Unfortunately, this does not coincide with the optimum antenna performance. Another more popular method is to use a folded dipole (**Fig 4.6(a)**)for the driven element. As the feed impedance of an ordinary dipole is likely to be in the region of 10Ω (when the antenna performance has been optimised), the impedance-quadrupling effect of using a folded dipole often provides a good solution. By using a larger diameter conductor in the unbroken arm of the dipole (ie the arm that is not broken to apply the power from the feeder), higher values of impedance transformation can be obtained.

Fig 4.6: Commonly-used matching methods employed at VHF and UHF.

Other methods of feeding the antenna include delta- and gamma-matches. The delta-match involves 'fanning out' the connection to the driven element (see **Fig 4.6(b)**). This method has the advantage that the driven element does not need to be broken to apply the feed as shown. As this is really applicable to a balanced feeder, a balun is required if coaxial cable is to be used.

A gamma match (**Fig 4.6(c)**)is another alternative that is often used. The outer or braid of the coax feeder is connected directly to the centre of the driven element. This can be done because the RF voltage at the centre is zero at this point. The inner conductor of the feeder carrying the RF current is taken out along the driven element. The inductance of the arm is then tuned out by the variable capacitor. When adjusting the antenna design, both the variable capacitor and the point at which the arm contacts the driven element are adjusted. Once a value has been ascertained for the variable capacitor, its value can be measured and a fixed component inserted if required. Values around 100pF for the 6m band, 35 to 50pF for the 2m band and less than 35pF for the 70cm band are typical.

STACKING YAGIS

In order to increase the gain of a Yagi antenna system, it is possible to stack one above the other as mentioned in Chapter 1. This provides a number of advantages. The beam-width in the vertical plane is reduced, but this is perfectly acceptable because the maximum amount of power needs to be radiated parallel to the earth for all terrestrial applications (obviously for satellite operation the position is different). Unlike other methods of increasing antenna gain, stacking does not narrow the beam-width in the horizontal plane, and this has advantages in not making the heading setting too critical as already mentioned. Another advantage is that additional gain can be achieved without increasing the length of the antenna, and hence the turning circle. The gain that can be achieved is between 2 and 3dB.

The optimum vertical spacing between antennas of five elements or more is one wavelength. This may be difficult to achieve sometimes, especially on the lower frequency bands such as 6m and 4m. However, there is still a worthwhile level of gain to be achieved with spacings of $^1/_2\lambda$, although $^5/_8\lambda$ gives a marked improvement.

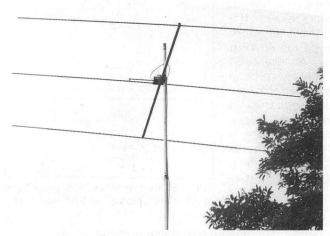

The PA3HBB / G0BZF 3-element 6m Yagi.

PA3HBB / G0BZF PORTABLE 3-ELEMENT 6m YAGI

This design (see the photograph)consists of a traditional three-element beam using the driven element, a reflector and one director. To reduce problems from static, it was designed as a single metal structure so that the whole of the antenna is at the same potential. To implement this, either a delta-match or a gamma-match is required, and in this case a gamma-match was chosen. This arrangement also enables the antenna to be more suitable for portable operation.

Start by assembling all the materials required. Most can be obtained from hardware or DIY stores. They include 2m lengths of 12.5mm-diameter aluminium tube for the centre sections, 10mm-diameter tube for the outer sections of the elements, a 1m-length of 10mm rod for the gamma section and a 2m-length of 25.4mm-square U-section aluminium for the boom.

Measure out and drill the holes for the reflector and director elements as shown in **Fig 4.7**. Mark and drill the 12.5mm holes with a smaller (6mm) bit before the larger holes are drilled. Take care to make sure these holes are straight and level in both directions, otherwise the elements will not be at right angles and the antenna will look very odd. Then, using a small round file, file a notch in the top side of each of the four holes, just large enough to pass through the head of the screw that will hold the 10mm-section tube in place. By doing this, assembly and dismantling for portable operation is made much easier. Drill a 2mm hole in the flat side of the

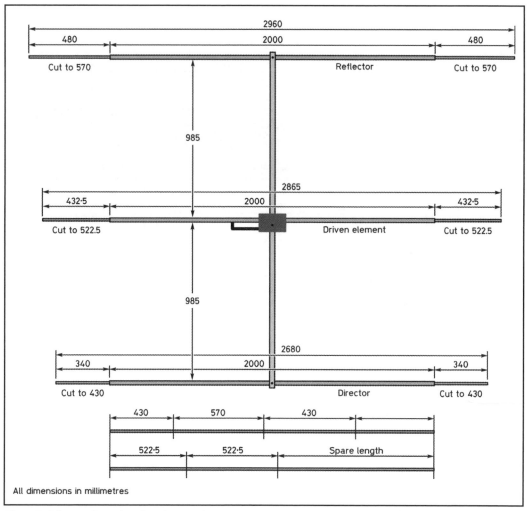

Fig 4.7: Dimensions for the three-element 50MHz antenna with dimensions and tube cutting directions.

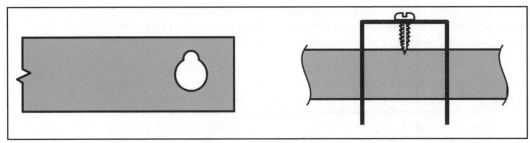

Fig 4.8: Details for the element holes for the reflector and director.

boom, on the element centre line. This is for the screw that holds the elements in place as shown in **Fig 4.8**.

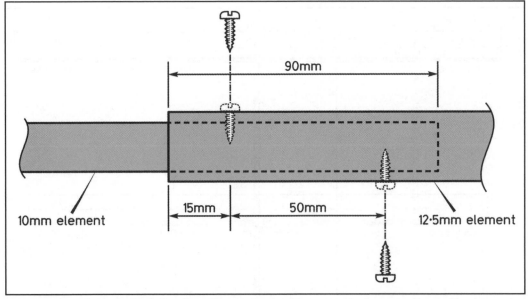

Fig 4.9: The method of joining the director and reflector end pieces to the main elements.

The reflector and director elements themselves are made up relatively easily. Cut the 10mm tubing carefully to the right length, and insert it into the 2m-length of 12.5mm tubing used for the reflector and director elements. Once adjusted to the correct length, drill a 2mm hole through the 12.5mm and 10mm sections where they join. This is so they they can be secured firmly in place using a screw as shown in **Fig 4.9**. It is best to secure these in position only after the antenna has been successfully tested and adjusted.

The driven element is made from the same materials as the reflector and director. A plastic weatherproof box is used as part of the driven element assembly to house the feeder termination and the 50pF capacitor for the gamma feed assembly. The fixing screw that goes through the box into the boom allows the driven element 12.5mm tubing to go parallel to the boom for easy transportation.

At this stage the 10mm and 12.5mm tubing are not yet joined together. This is to enable the tubing to fit tightly into the connection box. Holes must be drilled in the 12.5mm tubing of the driven element for the gamma-match arm. These holes allow the gamma-match arm to be secured by a screw inside the tubing as shown in **Fig 4.10**. A small hole (2mm) is drilled in one side of the tubing for the screw itself, and a larger hole (8mm) is drilled in the other side. This allows access for a screwdriver and to place the screw in the hole in the first place. After fitting and testing, the 8mm hole can be filled with putty or just taped over with weatherproof tape. To obtain the correct location of the gamma-match arm holes, first find the exact centre of the driven element and then measure out 305mm. This is the centre line for the holes. At the centre of the element, another 2mm hole must be drilled for the shield or outer connection of the coax cable.

The connection box needs to be drilled to take the driven element, gamma-match arm and the rotor of the matching capacitor. Carefully mark the positions and drill those for the driven element. Drill a 6mm (or thereabouts) pilot hole first, then the 12.5mm final hole. In this way, the position of the hole can be controlled far more precisely. Then drill a hole for the gamma-match arm. This is 40mm away from the element hole and, of course, only one hole is required. Next insert the driven element, and the 1m aluminium gamma-match rod into the box and select a suitable position for the capacitor. This is not critical and should be chosen so that it does not interfere with any of the other components in the box. Care

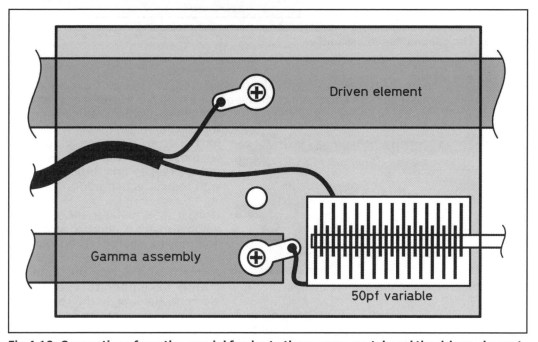

Fig 4.10: Connections from the coaxial feeder to the gamma-match and the driven element.

should be taken to ensure that the vanes of the capacitor do not touch any other component in the box as they are rotated. A hole is required for the fixing arm and any other mounting points to secure it firmly in place. Another hole is needed to secure the connection box to the boom. The screw for this will go through the box, and into the boom from the top side. A final hole is required for the coaxial feeder. Drill this in the same end as the hole for the gamma match arm.

To prepare the gamma-match arm, take the 1m rod, measure and cut it off 320mm. At one end, drill a 2mm hole for the connection point of the capacitor. Ninety degrees from this, at the other end of the rod, drill a 2mm hole straight through the rod. Using a 6mm bit, drill half-way through the rod to make a countersunk hole as shown in **Fig 4.11**. This is the attachment point for the gamma-match connecting arm.

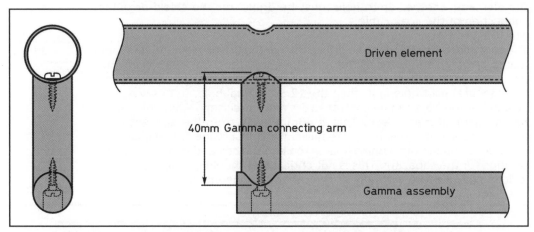

Driven element

40mm Gamma connecting arm

Gamma assembly

Fig 4.11: The gamma match assembly.

Using the remaining length of aluminium rod, cut a section exactly 40mm long. File both ends, one to fit the gamma match arm and the other to fit the driven element. In each end of this section a 2mm hole is required for the screw fixing. An alternative, for those with a workshop, is to use a drill press to drill through the rod with the correct size drill.

Photo: Construction of the gamma match.

Using a sheet metal screw, screw the gamma-match connecting arm to the gamma-match rod. Then place a screw through the hole in the driven element and screw the gamma-match assembly to the driven element. Next, slide the connection box over the driven element, and insert the gamma-match rod into the box until the box is in the centre of the element (**Fig 4.12**). Now screw the end pieces into the driven element in the same way that was used for the reflector and director. Fit the capacitor to the box and connect one side to the gamma-match assembly using the 2mm hole and a solder tag held in place by the sheet metal screw. Feed the coaxial cable into the box from the outside and strip the ends ready for connection. Solder the braid to the solder tag on the driven element and the inner conductor to one connection of the capacitor. The other one is connected to the gamma match. All work in the connection box is now complete.

To fix the driven element to the antenna boom, first drill a 2mm hole in the exact centre of the bottom flat edge of the boom U-section. The connection box is then screwed into this using a sheet metal screw. Turn the assembly over and align the driven element and gamma-match arm so that they are at right angles to the boom. Then, drill a second hole through the base of the connection box and into the U-section. This holds the driven element at the correct angle when the beam is being used.

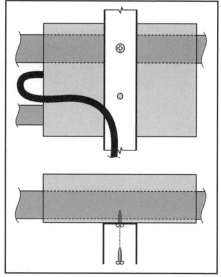

Fig 4.12: Fixing the connection box to the antenna boom.

To weatherproof the antenna, fill the ends of the elements with epoxy or a similar weatherproof material to prevent water entering the elements.

Once all the connections have been checked and the performance of the antenna has been assessed, close the connection box and seal it.

Finally, holes can be drilled in the side of the boom U-section to take U-clamps for mounting the antenna to a mast.

Once complete, the antenna can be checked and adjusted. This should

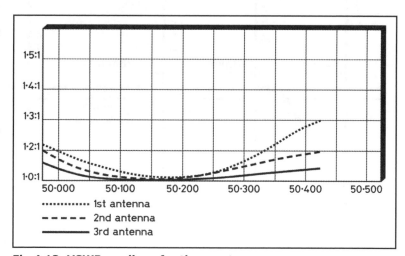

Fig 4.13: VSWR readings for three antennas.

be done with the antenna mounted at least 3m off the ground and in the clear. While the antenna should exhibit a low VSWR, the variable capacitor in the connection box will require setting. This should be done using a good VSWR bridge. Small adjustments can be made, checking the performance at the band edges as well as in the centre to obtain the best performance. The results for three antennas are given in **Fig 4.13**.

Assembly and dismantling of the beam is relatively quick and easy. Start by setting out all the metal parts in a clear flat area. Rotate the driven element through 90° and insert the retaining screw through the boom into the driven element. Slide the director through the boom and lock it in place using the retaining screw used in the first assembly. Repeat this process for the reflector, making sure to use the correct elements in the correct place. Dismantling is the reverse of assembly. Simply remove the three screws from the boom. This enables the two parasitic elements to

Parts list

Boom section	One 2m length 25.4 x 25.5mm square U-aluminium
Element centres	Three 2m lengths 12.5mm outside diameter aluminium tubing
Element ends	Two 2m lengths 10mm outside diameter aluminium tubing
Connection box	Plastic box 70 x 122 x 50mm
Variable capacitor	50pF
Miscellaneous	Solder tags, sheet metal screws

Table 4.1: Parts list for the 50MHz antenna.

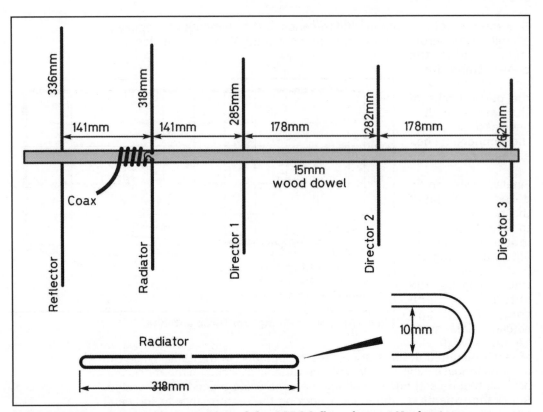

Fig 4.14: Dimensions and construction of the G3ROO five-element Yagi antenna.

be removed and the driven element to be swivelled round for easy transport. All that is required for assembly and dismantling of the antenna itself is a screwdriver for the three screws.

Assembled, the antenna weighs less than 3kg and packs neatly together. This makes it very easy to transport and an ideal portable unit.

G3ROO FIVE-ELEMENT 70cm YAGI

This beam is simple to construct and can be made relatively cheaply while still providing good results. The elements are constructed from 3.2mm brazing rod and the boom uses a 15mm wooden dowel. By using a wooden boom, the element fixing can be greatly simplified, thereby reducing the need for any specialist metalwork.

The driven element and coaxial connection on the G3ROO Yagi.

The basic dimensions are given in **Fig 4.14**. The first part of the construction entails marking the boom and drilling holes using a 3mm drill. Cut The brazing rods to length and taper them slightly at the end to enable them to be fed through the holes easily. The radiator, or driven element, presents a minor problem as it is folded. One way to achieve this is to bend one end first, push the element through the boom, and then bend the other section. To make the bending operation easier, the rod can be heated to the point where it becomes easier to bend. Obtaining the correct shape is easy. A large drill, nine or ten millimetres in diameter can be used as a former. Once in place and bent, the length should be rechecked and any necessary adjustments can be carefully made with a pair of pliers, and by applying some more heat.

Once the elements are all in place, add the feeder. Solder the two ends to the brazing rod, and then wind the feeder around the boom to form a four-turn choke to act

A suitable mast clamp for the Yagi.

as a balun. Take the feeder back along the boom to the mounting point, and secure it with tie wraps.

REFERENCES AND FURTHER READING

[1]   'A Portable 3-element 6 m Yagi', D A Reid, PA3HBB, *RadCom,* Nov 97 (RSGB).

[2]   'Novice Notebook: A Yagi for 70 cm', Ian Keyser, G3ROO, *RadCom*, Aug 95 (RSGB).

Chapter 5
The Cubical Quad

In this Chapter
- THE QUAD ANTENNA
- CURRENT AND VOLTAGE WAVEFORMS
- ELEMENT SPACING
- GAIN
- EASY 3-ELEMENT QUAD FOR 2m
- G3ROO 6m TWO-ELEMENT QUAD

The Cubical Quad, or Quad for short, is an antenna that finds uses mainly within amateur radio. For many years it has been a favourite of HF enthusiasts and, in the 1980s in particular, it found considerable interest amongst VHF addicts. The idea for the quad appeared in the 1940s and, since its introduction, there has always been considerable debate about its advantages compared with the more familiar Yagi. What is true is that it offers a gain of about 2dB over a Yagi of a similar length. This means that the quad compares with a pair of stacked Yagis as there is always some loss in the feed arrangements for stacking the two antennas. Another point that is often raised is that a quad is less affected by nearby objects, giving it an edge over the Yagi in many installations, especially those that are inside, possibly in the loft or attic.

THE QUAD ANTENNA
The basic quad element can be seen to be derived from two dipole elements stacked one above the other and fed in phase. This arrangement in itself gives gain because of the phasing effect between the two dipoles. The next stage in the development is to retain the two separate dipoles but bend the ends together. The voltages at the ends of the antennas are in phase with one another, and as a result it is possible to connect these ends together and remove one of the feeders to create the basic quad element. The loop forming the element is a full wavelength with each side being a quarter of a wavelength, as shown in **Fig 5.1**.

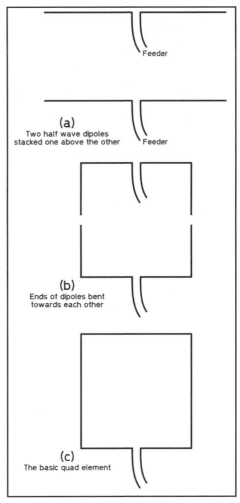

(a)
Two half wave dipoles
stacked one above the other

Feeder
Feeder

(b)
Ends of dipoles bent
towards each other

(c)
The basic quad element

Fig 5.1: The development of the quad.

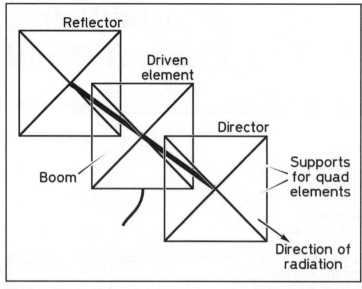

Fig 5.2: The basic quad antenna.

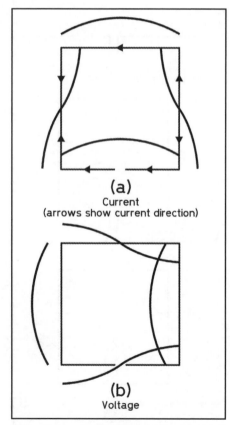

Fig 5.3: Voltage and current distributions on a quad element.

It is possible to have the basic element either as a horizontal square or turned through 45°. Sometimes this can be a more attractive option for construction. Both of these configurations produce a horizontally-polarised signal. To generate a vertically-polarised signal, the whole antenna should be rotated through 90° so that the feed-point is at the central point of the vertical section of the 'square' version or in one of the 'side' corners of the 'diamond' version.

The basic quad element consists of a loop of wire 1λ long in the form of a square as already described. As with the Yagi, parasitic elements can be added to make the antenna more directional as shown in **Fig 5.2**. A reflector can be added behind the driven element. To give the right phasing of the currents in the elements for it to reflect, it should be made inductive by tuning it below resonance by making the reflector slightly longer than the electrical full wavelength. Typically, it is made between 3 and 5% longer. An alternative method is to insert a short-circuit stub. This has the advantage that the element can be made exactly the same size as the driven element, and this may have some mechanical advantages.

Directors can also be made. They need to be capacitive to have the right current phasing and this can be achieved by tuning the element above resonance and making the element slightly shorter than the electrical full wavelength. Similarly, directors can also use a stub to give the required characteristics, but in this case an open-circuit stub is used.

CURRENT AND VOLTAGE WAVEFORMS

From the development of the basic quad element, it is fairly easy to deduce where the current and voltage maxima will be. As the current maximum is at the feed-point of a dipole, the same is also true for the quad, as shown in **Fig 5.3**. There is also another current maximum on the opposite side of the loop to the feed-point, ie where the second feed-point would have been. The voltage maxima appear at points a quarter of a wavelength away from the feed-point, ie where the two ends of the dipole would have been. It is often advisable not to position any fixings at the voltage points.

ELEMENT SPACING

Element spacing played a large part in the design of the Yagi, and the same is found for the quad. In general, a spacing of around 0.15λ to 0.2λ is used. This conveniently gives a feed impedance of around 50Ω. If a two-element quad has a spacing of just over a quarter of a wavelength, the feed impedance rises to around 75Ω. This is convenient for antennas used for VHF FM broadcast reception. If the spacing is reduced below about 0.15λ, the impedance falls and some form of impedance transformation would be required to enable the antenna to be fed by standard coax.

The spacing also has some effect on the gain. However, as in the case of the Yagi, the effect is fairly small, and impedance matching is the major requirement while adjusting the spacing.

GAIN

The basic quad element, being essentially a pair of stacked dipoles has a slight gain over a single dipole, generally about 2dB. A quad performs in a very similar way to a Yagi in terms of additional gain for extra elements. A reflector adds about 5dB gain and a director about an additional 2dB. Further directors average out at giving very approximately 1dB each. This means that a quad having the same number of elements as a Yagi will have about 2dB further gain. In fact, the comparison should be made between antennas having a similar length and designed to have optimum element spacing.

For similar gain antennas, the quad obviously presents a larger area to the wind because the basic element size is greater. This does mean that quad antennas are more prone to wind damage, and as a result they have tended to fall out of favour. Any that are built should be sturdily constructed if they are to be used outside.

EASY 3-ELEMENT QUAD FOR 2m

A quad for internal use can be made quite simply by constructing a simple wooden frame, as shown in **Fig 5.4**. Each element is made up from a cross of available wood approximately 13 x 13mm ($^1/_2$in by $^1/_2$in). At both ends of each piece of wood a small slot is cut to accommodate the wire. While the different elements must be different electrical sizes to make the antenna directional, this is best done by making each element the same physical size but altering the electrical length by the use of stubs. This will mean that the exact length of each cross-member is 720mm. However, it is best to make each one slightly longer and then adjust the size of the slot to enable the wire length to be altered for trimming the antenna to resonance.

Make the frame as rigid as possible. Standard woodworking joints are quite adequate and there should not be the need for extra reinforcement if the antenna is to be used inside. Then fit the wire on the wood. It

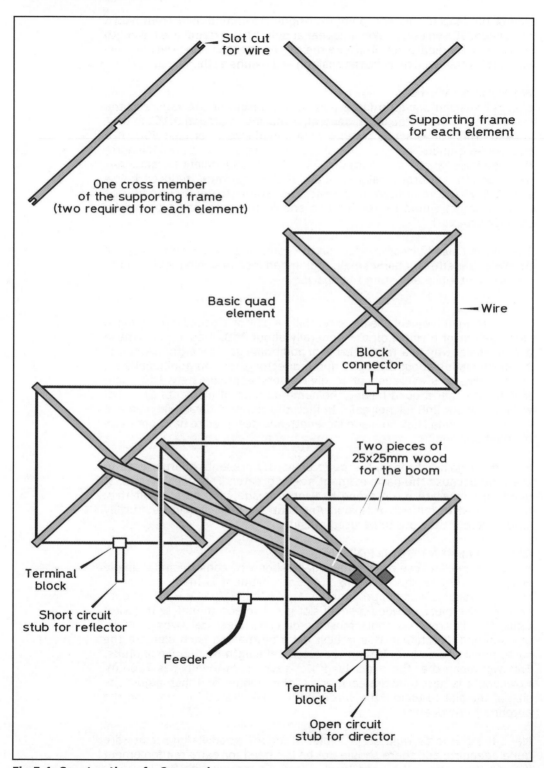

Slot cut
for wire

One cross member
of the supporting frame
(two required for each element)

Supporting frame
for each element

Basic quad
element

Wire

Block
connector

Two pieces of
25x25mm wood
for the boom

Terminal
block

Short circuit
stub for reflector

Feeder

Terminal
block

Open circuit
stub for director

Fig 5.4: Construction of a 2m quad.

should be as thick as reasonably possible to maintain a reasonable bandwidth. 12SWG or 14SWG is quite suitable. Then terminate the open end using a terminal block. This provides a method of keeping the antenna wire in place as well as a method of connecting the coax.

The reflector and director each use a stub. This consists of a pair of lengths of wire about 75mm long. One wire is attached in the same place as the coax connection is made on the driven element. In the case of the reflector, the stub is short-circuited, whereas the stub for the director is left open circuit.

Make the antenna boom out of two lengths of 25 x 25mm wood. They are mounted as shown in Fig 5.4. If necessary, the spacing of the parasitic elements can be adjusted with these two lengths of wood acting as a clamp. Once all the adjustments have been made, firmly screw and glue all of the elements to the boom.

G3ROO 6m TWO-ELEMENT QUAD

This arose from a need for a rugged antenna that outstripped the performance of the designer's three-element Yagi. It achieved these requirements, having a very slight increase in gain while offering a wider beam-width and making orientation easier.

Construction is straightforward and uses a piece of 5mm aluminium plate, nylon cable ties and fibreglass rods as seen in the photograph.

A total of eight rods or spacers are used. Four shorter ones, each 1080mm long, are used for the driven element and four longer ones, 1110mm long, are used for the reflector. The essential constructional details are shown in **Fig 5.5**. First, drill

The two-element 6m quad in position.

the aluminium plate as detailed. Next, loosely fit the fibreglass rods in place with cable ties. Drill holes about 6mm from the ends of the rods and 90° from the plane of the loop. By doing this, the wire will not slip when under tension, thereby preserving the symmetry of the loop.

Measure the wire lengths carefully, adding about 30mm for soldering the ends. The loops are made from normal multi-strand hook up wire, although thicker wire can be used without materially affecting the performance. The driven loop has a wire length of 5430mm and the reflector, 5940mm. This should be cut to length but not assembled on the rods at this stage.

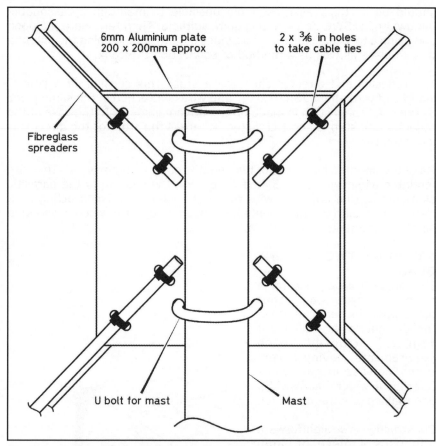

Fig 5.5: Construction details for the basic quad, showing the fibre glass spreaders attached to the aluminium plate with nylon cable ties.

A gamma-match is used to provide a good match to the antenna and this is made up on a piece of perspex, using the wire from some 2.5mm earth cable. Construct this by folding the wire into a hairpin 310mm long and

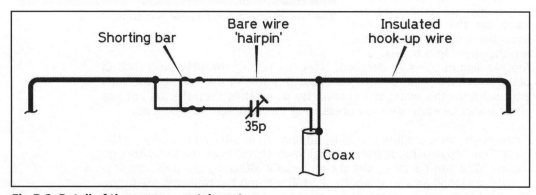

Fig 5.6: Detail of the gamma-match system.

with a 20mm spacing as shown in **Fig 5.6**. The thickness of the wire and the small size enables it to be supported only by a piece of Perspex at the capacitor and feed-point as shown in the photograph. A capacitance of around 20pF is required, so a 35 or 50pF trimmer is used to provide the required capacitance.

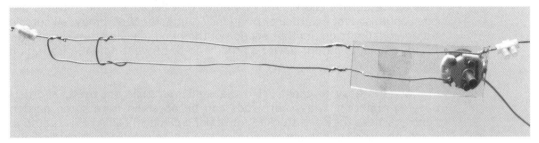

Close-up of the gamma-match, showing the shorting link on the left.

Feed the reflector loop through the holes at the ends of the four longer rods, and solder the two ends together. Next attach the driven wire to one side of the gamma-match and pass the free ends of the wire through the holes of the shorter rods. Complete the loop by soldering the loose ends together. The gamma-match arrangement is shown in the photograph, although in the final version of the antenna, the capacitor was contained within a small box to shelter it from the rain and the elements.

The wire is kinked through the ends of the rods to prevent slippage.

Finally, slide the rods in or out of the cable ties so that 700mm loop spacing is correct and then pull the cable ties fully tight. To make the structure even more rigid, the ends of the driven loop can be tied to the corresponding end of the reflector loop using fishing line.

The antenna does need some adjustment. Both the tapping point and the capacitor require adjustment for the minimum level of SWR. It is also necessary to ensure that the feeder is kept perpendicular to the horizontal part of the driven element, and equidistant from the vertical sections. If the feeder is moved one way or the other, the SWR will rise rapidly, demonstrating the need to keep the antenna system symmetrical.

On the original antenna system, the gamma-match was adjusted with the base of the quad mounted about 8ft in the air to remove the effect of the ground and simulate the conditions when the antenna would be in its final position. The adjustments were then made standing on a ladder. The shorting bar on the gamma-match was moved about 5mm at a time along the hairpin starting from the closed end (ie furthest away from the capacitor). The capacitor was also adjusted for minimum VSWR. Once adjusted, the antenna was mounted on the side of the house and it was found that the resonant frequency rose by about 100kHz and the VSWR rose to 1.2:1. This change may be important because if the antenna has been optimised for a particular frequency range, the VSWR may fall outside acceptable limits on another section of the band, causing the transmitter PA to reduce its output power as many do to prevent damage from high levels of VSWR.

The quad is easy to construct if the right materials are used, and it is easy to maintain. Glass-fibre rods can be obtained from some garden centres where they are stocked for making cloches. Failing this, bamboo could be used, but these would need to be selected for thickness and flexibility so that the required final shape is obtained.

Parts list (Dimensions in mm)

Glass fibre rods	8 or 10mm-diameter, 4 x 1080mm long, 4 x 1110mm long
Aluminium plate	200 x 300, 5mm thick
2 x 50mm U-bolts	Antenna fixing types are preferable
12 x 5mm nylon cable ties	Several spares are advisable
Variable capacitor	50pF
Copper wire	1m solid 2.5mm - see text
Multi-strand hook up wire	12m

Table 5.1: Parts list for the 2m quad.

REFERENCE

[1]   'A two-element 6m quad', Ian Keyser, G3ROO, *RadCom* (RSGB), Aug 1997.

Chapter 6
Vertical Antennas

In this Chapter
- QUARTER-WAVE VERTICAL
- FOLDED ELEMENT
- RADIATION PATTERN
- $^5/_8\lambda$ VERTICAL
- G3ROO 430MHz $^5/_8\lambda$ VERTICAL
- THE COLINEAR ANTENNA
- J-ANTENNAS
- 'ROOSTICK' VHF J-ANTENNA
- PA0HMV TWIN-BAND VERTICAL ANTENNA
- RUBBER DUCK ANTENNA
- CAR-MOUNTING OF VERTICAL ANTENNAS

Vertical antennas find widespread use in the VHF and UHF portions of the spectrum. You only have to look at the antennas that are used on cars to see this. Private mobile radio (PMR), cell phones, amateur radio and a number of other users all employ vertical antennas, particularly for mobile communications. The reason for this widespread use is the omnidirectional radiation pattern that they give in the horizontal plane. This means that the antennas do not have to be re-orientated to maximise the signals as the car moves.

Although vertical antennas find widespread use on cars, they are used in many other situations as well. In fact, they are used in any application which needs a non-directional antenna.

There are several different types of vertical. The quarter-wavelength antenna is the most basic form, but each different type has its own advantage. One enhancement to the basic quarter-wave antenna is made by extending its length. By doing this, it is possible to concentrate more of the power into a lower angle of radiation. Another method of having a low angle of radiation is to have a number of different radiating elements above one another. If they are fed in the correct phase, the antenna can be made to have quite a significant gain over a standard quarter-wave vertical.

QUARTER-WAVE VERTICAL
Like the name suggests, the antenna consists of a quarter-wavelength vertical element as shown in **Fig 6.1**. The voltage and current waveforms show that, at the end of the antenna, the voltage rises to a maximum, whereas the current falls to a minimum. Then, at the base of the antenna, at the feed-point, the voltage is at a minimum and the current is at its maximum. This gives the antenna a low feed impedance, typically around 20Ω.

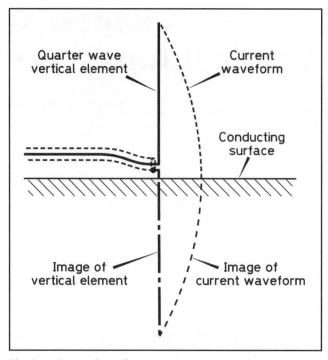

Fig 6.1: Operation of a quarter-wave vertical.

To enable the antenna to operate, a ground plane is required. Ideally, this is a perfectly-conducting plane which serves to 'mirror' the vertical section of the antenna. If these ground plane elements are bent downwards from the horizontal, the feed impedance will be raised. A 50Ω match will be achieved when the angle between the ground plane rods and the horizontal is around 42°. Another solution is to include an impedance-matching element in the antenna. Normally, this is in the form of a tapped coil that can be conveniently housed at the base of the antenna.

In theory, the ground plane used for the antenna should extend out to infinity. However, in practice, the ground plane is normally simulated quite satisfactorily by a number of rods about a quarter-wavelength long, extending out from the base as shown in **Fig 6.2**. This is normally quite adequate for the majority of applications, and four radials normally suffice. Only rarely are any more used at VHF or UHF. In some instances, the rods may be joined mechanically around the periphery to increase mechanical stability. If the mechanical restraints also have an electrical connection then this has the effect of increasing the electrical size of the ground plane structure and therefore the length of the radials can be reduced by about 5%.

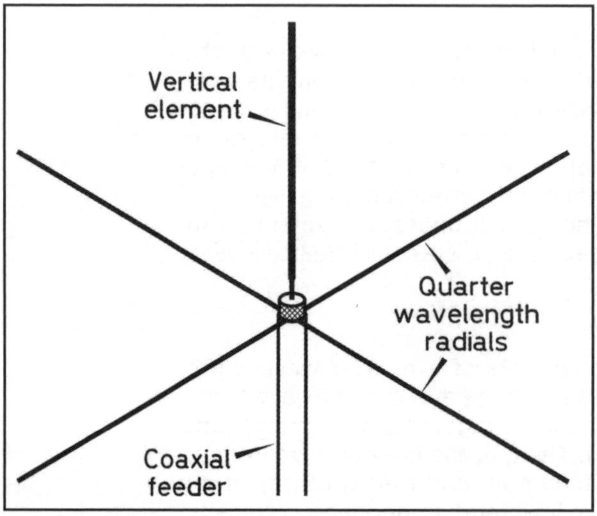

When space is at a premium, it is possible to reduce the size of the radial system. This can be done as shown in **Fig 6.3** by bending the radials into a circle. When this is done, the radial section L1 should be about 0.07λ. The circumference of the circle should then be about 0.43λ. This type of arrangement also has the advantage that it can be made to be more rugged than conventional radials, but it has the disadvantage of a much narrower bandwidth than an antenna with conventional radials. The feed impedance is also low.

Fig 6.2: A quarter-wave vertical antenna system.

For mobile applications, the car body metalwork acts as an ideal ground plane. This means there is no need for any radials and it makes the vertical an ideal antenna for mobile use.

FOLDED ELEMENT
In view of the low impedance presented to the feeder by the ground plane antenna, methods must be found of presenting a good match, and some have already been outlined. Another is to use a folded element (**Fig 6.4**). In the same way that a folded dipole increases the feed impedance of the antenna, so a folded vertical element can be used. If the diameter of each section is the same, an increase is achieved in the ratio of 4:1. This would bring the impedance to 80Ω which provides an acceptable match to 75Ω feeder. By using a smaller diameter grounded element, the feed impedance can be reduced so that a good match to 50Ω coax can be achieved.

RADIATION PATTERN
One of the major advantages of the vertical antenna is that it radiates equally in all directions around it. In operation, it appears to have the bottom half reflected in the ground plane, producing an antenna that is substantially the same as the single dipole. Theory shows that if the antenna were placed above a perfectly-conducting infinitely-large ground, all of the radiation associated with the lower half of the antenna

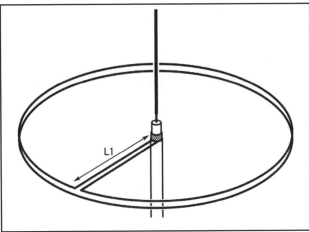

Fig 6.3: An alternative radial system for a vertical.

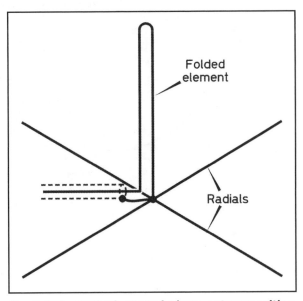

Fig 6.4: A vertical ground-plane antenna with a folded element.

would be radiated by the top half, giving a 3dB improvement. In practice, the ground plane is never infinitely-large and has losses, so this means that the theoretical improvement is never fully realised. A typical radiation pattern might be like that shown in **Fig 6.5**. *See over page*

It is also found that, as the size of the ground plane increases, the angle of radiation rises, leaving an angle between the ground plane and the main lobe of radiation, as shown in **Fig 6.6**. *See over page*

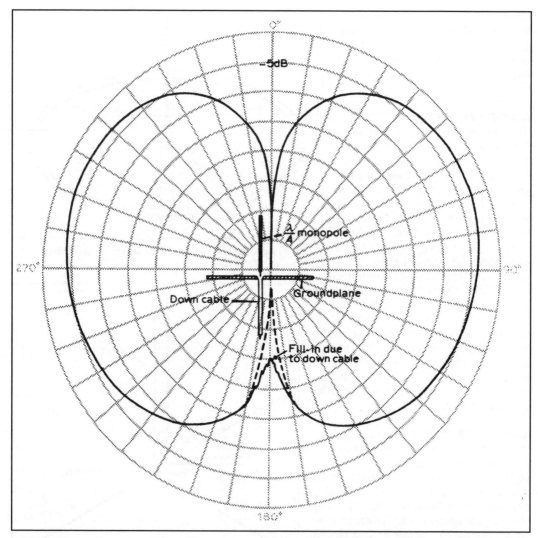

Fig 6.5: Polar diagram of a quarter-wave vertical over a half-wave square ground plane.

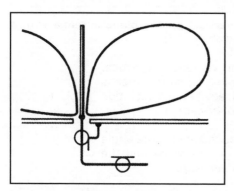

Fig 6.6: Radiation pattern of a whip antenna on a large ground plane.

A 70cm VERTICAL

A quarter-wave vertical antenna can be made very easily for a minimal cost. An example of a vertical for the 70cm amateur band is shown in **Fig 6.7**. The antenna can be constructed from 18SWG copper wire. While this gauge was used in the prototypes and is sufficiently rigid for internal use, it is not particularly critical. Almost any suitable wire can be used, although thicker wire will be more rigid and will give a slightly wider bandwidth.

The simplest way to construct the antenna is simply to solder the wires directly onto the coax. However other more ingenious methods can be used as well. One is to use a connector as the base of the antenna as shown in **Fig 6.8**. By doing this, a more rigid base is provided and the antenna can be easily disconnected when not in use.

The construction of the antenna is quite simple although a few notes may be helpful. The radials should be bent slightly down from the position shown in the diagram. This

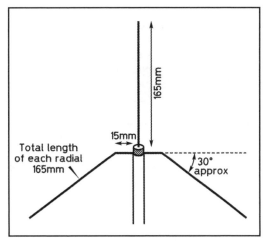

Fig 6.7: A quarter-wave vertical for the 70cm amateur band.

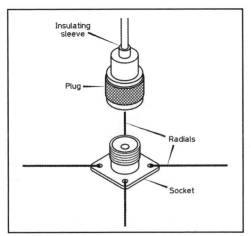

Fig 6.8: The use of a connector as the antenna base.

is done to ensure a good match to the 50Ω coax and final adjustments to the radials should bring the SWR reading

down to virtually 1:1 if it is to be used for transmitting. Using this antenna, a number of contacts were made over some reasonable distances.

$^5/_8\lambda$ VERTICAL

If a half-wave dipole is extended in length, the radiation at right angles to the antenna starts to increase before finally splitting into several lobes. The maximum radiation occurs when the dipole is about 1.2λ. When used as a vertical radiator against a ground plane, the element length is just over 0.6λ ($^5/_8\lambda$). This type of antenna has become very popular. By extending the length of the vertical element in this way, the amount of power radiated at a low angle is increased, and a $^5/_8\lambda$ vertical has a gain of close to 4dBd (ie +4dB relative to a dipole). To achieve this gain, the antenna must be constructed of the right materials so that losses are reduced to the absolute minimum

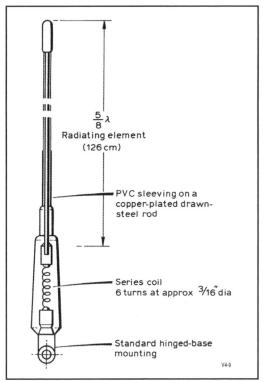

Fig 6.9: Construction of a typical $^5/_8\lambda$ antenna.

and the overall performance is maintained, otherwise much of the advantage of using the additional length will be lost.

It is necessary to ensure that the antenna provides a good match to 50Ω coaxial cable. It is found that a $^3/_4\lambda$ wavelength vertical element provides a good match, and therefore the solution is to make the $^5/_8\lambda$ radiator have the 'electrical length' of a $^3/_4\lambda$ element. This is achieved by placing a small loading coil at the base of the antenna (**Fig 6.9**) to increase its electrical length. Ideally this coil should be kept rigid and not bent as the antenna flexes if it is mounted on a moving car. Otherwise the match to the feeder will change and the operation will be impaired.

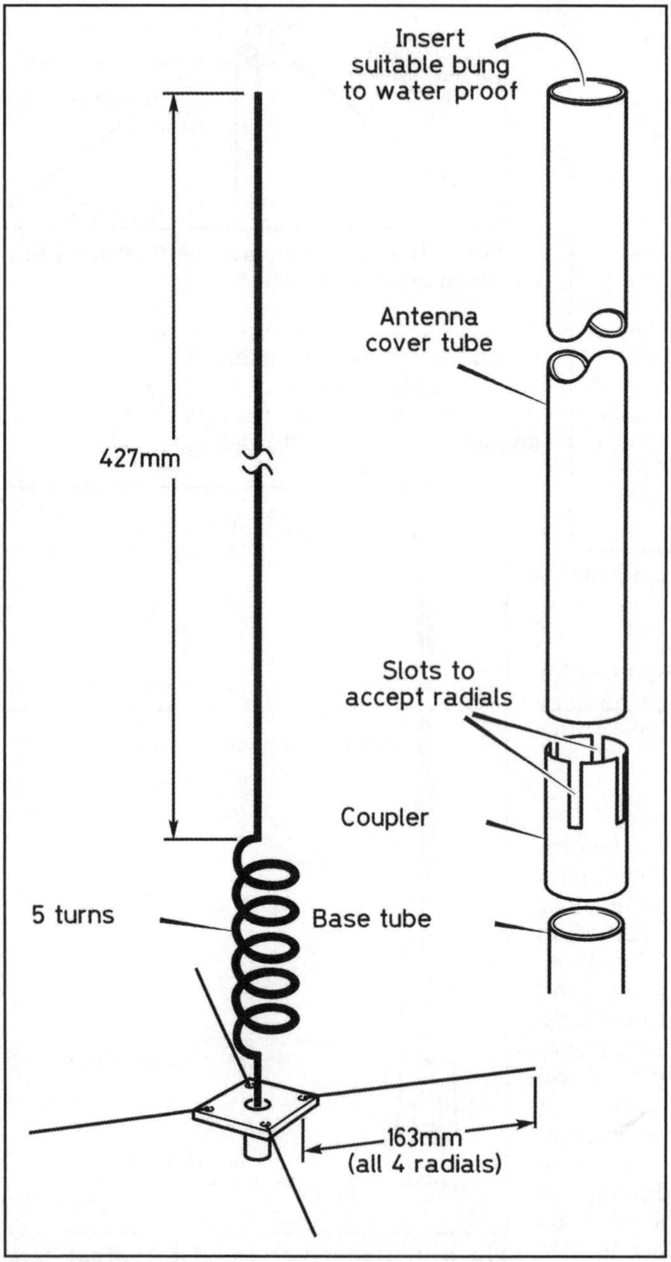

G3ROO 430MHz $^5/_8\lambda$ VERTICAL

The antenna can be made quite readily and consists of a $^5/_8\lambda$ vertical radiator with a loading coil to make it look like a $^3/_4\lambda$ antenna to the feeder. This gives it a low impedance and can be made to present a good match to the feeder. It is based around a length of 1.5mm brazing rod that is used for the radiating element. The basic form is shown in **Fig 6.10**.

Cut a length of brazing rod sufficiently long to make the radiator and the five-turn coil at the bottom, as shown in the photograph. Wind the coil on a 4mm drill shank to give it the correct diameter. If this makes the antenna too 'whippy', a short length of *plastic* knitting needle can be inserted into the coil. Solder the radiator into the centre connection of a four-hole BNC socket. Cut four lengths of 3mm welding rod. One end is bent at right angles to allow it to be inserted into the BNC socket fixing hole and

Fig 6.10: Construction of the 430MHz vertical antenna.

soldered as shown. Once firmly in place, trim the rod to length.

To protect the antenna from water, use a length of 22mm PVC waste pipe of the 'weldable' variety, available from plumbers' merchants. Slot a coupler section to accommodate the radials and file the BNC socket so that it slides down inside the coupler with the radials protruding from the slots as shown. Cut a length of waste pipe 30mm longer than the antenna, place it over the radiator and push it into the coupler. Use a plastic bung to close the top end of the tube. A plastic screw top could be used instead.

The 430MHz $^5/_8\lambda$ vertical antenna showing the construction details.

In use, the antenna offered a standing wave ratio of 1:1. Before finally sealing the antenna in its tubing, it is worth checking the performance of the antenna while access is still available. Only when satisfied should it be finally sealed.

To seal, apply plastic weld solution to the joints and allow to set. While the weld is setting, it can help to tape over the joints with PVC tape to hold the antenna in place. Cut a further section of waste pipe and slide it over the bottom section of the coupler, holding it in place with a self-tapping screw. This enables the antenna to be mounted to a pole using standard fixings or even cable ties.

Parts list

1	four-hole mounting BNC socket
1m	3mm-diam brazing rod
1m	1.5mm-diam brazing rod
1m	22mm-diam PVC waste water pipe
1	22mm coupler
	Plastic welding solution

Table 6.1: Parts list for the 430MHz vertical.

The completed antenna in its plastic tube.

THE COLINEAR ANTENNA

Although vertical antennas are often used to achieve an omnidirectional pattern around the antenna, gain is still important. One way of achieving this is to stack dipoles vertically above each other to form an antenna known as a colinear. To illustrate how a colinear operates, take the case of a wire that is 2λ long. In this case the level of radiation will be poor as the successive current maxima are not in the same phase. If the magnitudes of all the current maxima were the same, they would cancel one another out and radiation at right angles to the wire would be zero (**Fig 6.11 (a)**). By ensuring that all the current maxima *are* in phase, radiation at right angles to the antenna is reinforced and gain is achieved

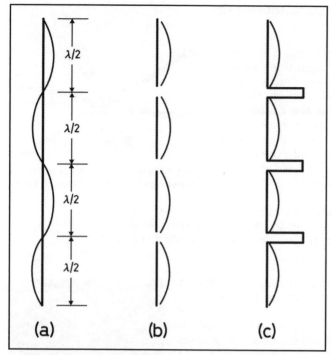

Fig 6.11: Current distributions on a wire showing how the colinear antenna is derived.

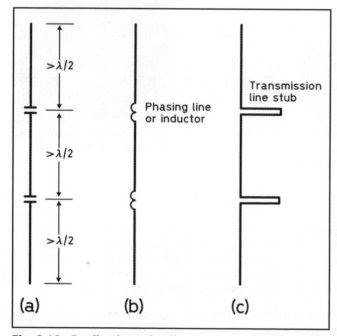

Fig 6.12: Realisation of colinear antennas. Note: the antennas are end-fed.

in this direction (**Fig 6.11(b)**). There are several ways of obtaining the correct phasing. One is to insert a non-radiating half-wavelength by using a transmission line (**Fig 6.11(c)**). This can be realised by using a quarter wavelength of ribbon cable that can be wound round the insulating element that is required between the two half wavelength radiating sections.

This is by no means the only method that can be used to obtain the correct phasing. A more subtle approach is to use radiating elements that are a little longer or shorter than half a wavelength. This makes the feed arrangements much easier, because end-feeding a half-wavelength antenna is difficult as a result of the very high feed impedance. The self-reactance of the element that is either longer or shorter than a half wavelength is then used in the design of the phasing network inserted between the elements. In this way, the correct phase shift can be conveniently inserted between the elements. Often the non-radiating transmission line can be replaced by a capacitor or inductor in series with the residual element as shown in **Figs 6.12(a)** and **(b)**. In some instances, it may be more convenient and cheaper to use a transmission line, especially if significant levels of RF power are likely to be used.

J-ANTENNAS

One of the major drawbacks of the standard vertical antenna is the fact that it requires a set of radials or a ground plane if it is to operate correctly. This is not always convenient and it can sometimes be difficult to obtain the best results from a car. From a fixed location, a set of radials increases the visual impact of the antenna and this may not be acceptable.

One solution to the problem is the J-antenna (**Fig 6.13**). In essence it is a form of Zepp (Zeppelin) antenna that found favour in the 1930s as an HF antenna. It consists of a half-wave radiating element which is end-fed using a quarter-wave stub of open wire or 300Ω balanced feeder used to match the impedance to the coaxial feeder.

As shown in the diagram, either leg of the quarter-wave stub can be fed. The resulting implementation of it is shown in Fig 6.13

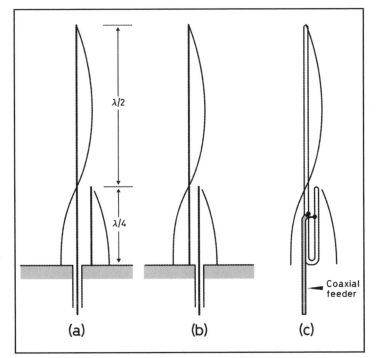

Fig 6.13: The J-antenna.

(c). This type of antenna is quite easy to construct and gives good results. The main disadvantage is that it can be a little more difficult to adjust than some other forms. The reason for this is that impedance matching has to be accomplished by altering the trimming length of the stub.

The length of the half-wave radiating stub can be determined using the same formula as used in calculating the length of a half-wave dipole. The physical length of the balanced feeder will depend on the velocity factor of the feeder in use. For open-wire feeder, the velocity factor is nearly unity and the length will be very close to that of the free-space quarter-wavelength. If 300Ω twin feeder is used, the length required will be shorter because its velocity factor is about 0.85.

'ROOSTICK' VHF J-ANTENNA

In view of the shape of the antenna and the callsign of the designer (G3ROO) this was given the name the 'Roostick' antenna. Its construction is very simple [1] and the details of the overall antenna can be seen in **Fig 6.14**.

To start the construction, first take a two-metre length of 300Ω ribbon feeder and measure 430mm from one end. Carefully cut *one* of the wires in the feeder at this point and remove this wire by snipping through the webs of the feeder. This creates the counterpoise section.

Remove some insulation from the cut wire and form it so that it can be bent round to meet the uncut wire. At this point, remove about 5mm of insulation so the two wires can be joined to form the point marked RF

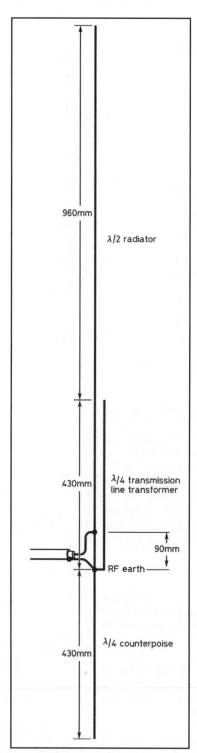

Fig 6.14: Details of the 'Roostick' antenna.

earth on the diagram. From this point, measure a further 430mm up the cable and cut on the same side of the feeder as before. Remove the cut wire from the remaining length of the feeder. Then trim the top cut end of the ribbon cable to 960mm to create the half wavelength radiating section.

The feed is accomplished by connecting the braid from the coaxial feeder with the shortest possible tail to the RF earth point. Then, carefully remove some insulation from the ribbon feeder 90mm from the earth point. Make sure this is done on the wire connected to the radiating element. Then connect the inner of the coax to this point.

The actual lengths detailed here are a little shorter than had been expected from calculations, and this gives an SWR reading of around 1.4:1 at 145MHz.

The antenna can be supported inside a 2m length of plastic water pipe with the coaxial feeder hanging down alongside the counterpoise. The bottom is left open but the top is sealed with a plastic cap. This arrangement prevents water entering but allows a way for condensation to escape. The antenna can be clamped to the supporting mast or pipe using the last 150mm.

PA0HMV TWIN-BAND VERTICAL ANTENNA

This design was originally published by Bert Veuskens, PA0HMV, in the April 1999 edition of *Electron*, the Netherlands Amateur Radio Society publication and then translated for *RadCom* [2]. The antenna acts as an end-fed half wave-radiator on 145MHz giving it a gain of 0dBd. Being a half-wave element, it has a high feed impedance and therefore a matching arrangement must be used to provide a good match to the 50Ω coax (see **Fig 6.15**). Often, a parallel tuned circuit with a tap in the coil is used to provide the correct transformation. However, as this antenna is for use

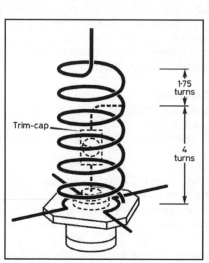

Fig 6.15: The matching section of the antenna.

on two bands, a different arrangement has been adopted here. Instead, the feed from the coax is placed in series with a variable capacitor making the coax look into a series tuned circuit, thereby voltage-feeding the antenna. On 435MHz, this acts as a high-pass filter and therefore appears transparent because operation is above the cut-off point.

On 435MHz, the antenna acts as two stacked $^5/_8\lambda$ radiators with a gain approaching 5dBd. To end-feed the antenna, the lower part must be extended electrically to $^3/_4\lambda$. This is achieved by adding 1.75 turns on top of the 145MHz coil. For operation at 435MHz, resonant radials are required, but as they are not resonant at 145MHz they do not affect the operation on the lower band.

To provide the correct phasing for the stacked sections, a phasing stub is inserted between them as shown in **Fig 6.16**.

To construct the antenna, first start by filing and / or sawing off the corners of the flange of the coax socket to enable it to fit snugly into the 28mm mounting tube. Drill a hole for the earthy end of the coil as shown in **Fig 6.17**. Pre-bend the two sets of adjacent radials, leaving the ends slightly long.

To solder the radials to the coax socket, a jig can be a great help. To make one, drill a 16mm-diameter hole in

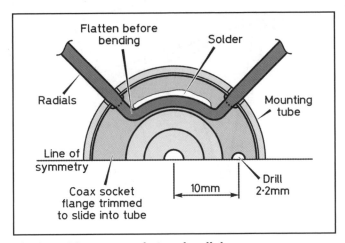

Fig 6.17: The coax socket and radials.

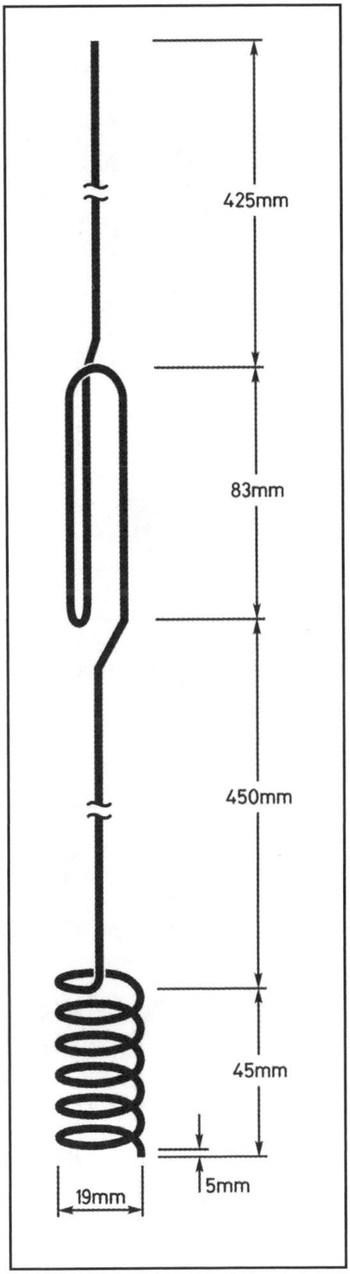

Fig 6.16: The shape and dimensions of the antenna wire.

the centre of a 25mm-square piece of chipboard, insert the coax socket, barrel down into the hole and place two sets of radials as shown in Figs 6.15 and 6.17. Then fix them to the chipboard. This can be done using staples. Next, solder them in place as shown. For this a 50W or larger

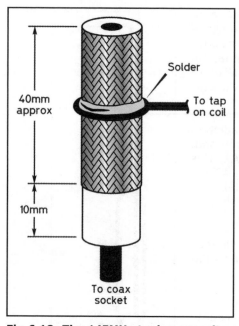

Fig 6.18: The 145MHz tuning capacitor can be made from RG-58 coax.

soldering iron will be needed. The connector will get very hot during this and it will retain its heat for some while, so care is necessary. It is also worth noting that professional-grade connectors will use PTFE for the centre insulator and this will not melt. Cheap versions may give a problem.

Next cut each radial to 173mm measured from the centre of the coax socket. Then, solder the 'cold' terminal of the tubular trimmer to the coax connector. It is worth noting that the capacitor can be made from an odd length of RG-58 coax as shown in **Fig 6.18**.

Once the work on the radials and the coax connector has been completed, work can commence on the radiating element itself. Unroll and stretch the antenna wire to straighten it out. Cut off 60cm and then, starting at one end, tightly wind six turns on a 19mm tube, rod or dowel. Stretch the coil to the shape and dimensions in Fig 6.16. Then solder the short end of the coil into the hole drilled in the flange of the coax socket and connect the other

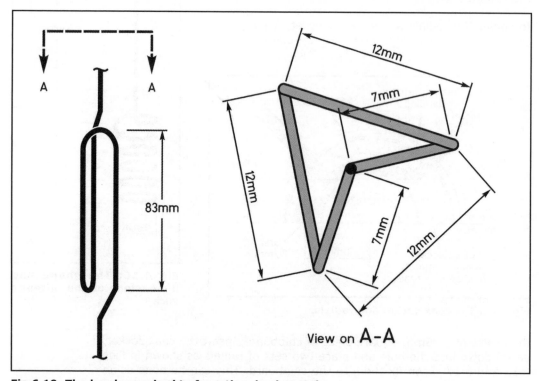

Fig 6.19: The bends required to form the phasing stub.

terminal of the trim cap to the coil, four turns above the earthy end. Approximately half the lower radiator section should now point up, coaxially with the coil.

With the remaining wire, shape the phasing section as shown in **Fig 6.19** using a 9.5mm drill as a former. Trim the lower wire end so that it makes up the 450mm shown in Fig 6.16 (two) when butt-spliced to the top of the wire on the coil. Slide the polystyrene foam centring disc on the wire below the phasing stub and butt-splice the two sections together. This is best done by soldering them into a short sleeve of copper tubing or possibly into the brass sleeve removed from the smallest size of chocolate

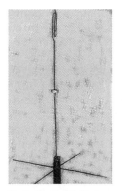

P A 0 H M V ' s prototype without its cover.

block connector but discard the screws as they will rust. Then cut the top wire to 460mm. This leaves some extra for pruning the antenna for resonance later. Slide the second centring disc on the top wire.

Saw and / or file four slots into one end of the 428mm copper pipe, each 90° apart and each 4mm wide by 7mm deep as shown in **Fig 6.20**. Do the same with one end of the PVC tubing but make the slots 70mm deep.

After assembly and tuning, the 28mm mounting tubing will be clamped to the top of the mast using commercial hardware.

It is necessary to tune the antenna for the best performance. The PVC weather shield lowers the resonant frequency by some 3MHz on 70cm. Accordingly, tuning the antenna for that band should be arranged to give the optimum performance 3MHz higher than the required frequency.

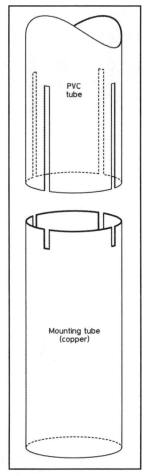

Fig 6.20: Slots for the four radials in the mounting tube and PVC cover.

Parts list

28 mm OD copper tube	220mm
PVC tube 32mm OD	
28mm ID with cap	1.2m
Jubilee clip	32 mm prefer stainless steel
Coax socket	N-type (preferred) with square flange 50Ω
Brass rod or tubing	3mm OD for 4 radials 720mm required
Bare copper wire	2.25mm-diam 1.6m required. 14SWG can be used as an alternative
Trim-cap tubular	10pF Tronsor or use RG-58 as described in the text
2 off Centring discs	polystyrene foam sliding in PVC tube
Sealing compound	

Table 6.2: Components list for the PA0HMV antenna.

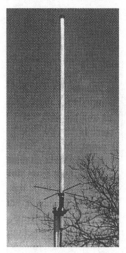

The finished antenna.

The tuning arrangement is fairly straightforward. Feed a short length of coaxial cable through the 28mm copper tube and connect it to the N-type connector. Push the socket into the copper pipe until each radial touches the bottom of the slot. Place the assembly well clear of other objects, and especially other wires or other conductors that might affect its performance, but keep it low enough to work on. Connect a 70cm signal source, eg a transceiver, through an SWR meter, and note the response. It should be found that the frequency producing the lowest SWR reading is lower than intended because the antenna was left slightly long internationally in construction. Carefully snip small bits off the top of the antenna to bring the resonant frequency (ie the frequency of lowest SWR) up to 438MHz or 3MHz above the required centre frequency. Then fix the two centring discs using a drop of epoxy glue at the voltage nodes, 170mm below the top of the antenna and half way between the top of the coil and bottom of the phasing section. Slide the PVC pipe down the antenna until each radial is squeezed between the bottom of its slot in the copper pipe and the top of the slot in the PVC pipe. At this point, verify that the minimum point of the SWR occurs sufficiently close to the required frequency and that it is below 1.5:1.

To tune the antenna for 145MHz operation, raise the PVC tube just enough to gain access to the trimmer capacitor and adjust it for best results at 145MHz or the centre frequency of operation. It was found that the capacitor made from the short coaxial section was adequate, but required the braid to be trimmed to provide adjustment.

With the tuning complete, the PVC tube should be pushed down into place, and fixed in position with a stainless steel jubilee clip below the radials. Place the cap on top of the PVC tube and weatherproof the antenna by applying sealing compound around the gaps in the PVC around the radials. Make sure that rain cannot enter the antenna and reach the capacitor, but leave space so that condensation has a way out.

RUBBER DUCK ANTENNA

Many hand-held transceivers use small antennas that are often referred to as 'rubber ducks'. They are helix antennas consisting of a length of spring wire wound such that the diameter of the spring is less than 0.1λ, and typically 0.01λ in diameter. These antennas become resonant when their axial length is around 0.1λ and in addition to this they can present manageable load impedances.

In view of their small electrical size, it is no surprise to find that resonance only occurs over a relatively small bandwidth. It is also heavily influenced by the sleeve that is normally fitted over the antenna, and also by the ground plane against which it is fed. This ground plane is normally the transceiver itself together with any hand capacitance. The current distribution along the antenna is similar to that of an ordinary whip antenna, but compressed into the much shorter length of the antenna.

For antennas for hand-held radios, the antenna is designed to be an electrical $\frac{5}{8}\lambda$. In this way, the current maximum occurs about a third of the way along the antenna. This helps improve the radiation efficiency and also helps minimise the variability of the ground plane.

A $^3/_4\lambda$ straight whip over a ground plane has a resistive match very close to 50Ω. If this is coiled into a helical spring it will resonate at a lower frequency, partly due to the capacitance between adjacent turns. The spring can then be trimmed to bring it back to resonance at the required frequency. Typically, the actual length of wire will be equivalent to between $^5/_8\lambda$ and $^1/_2\lambda$, although electrically it is $^3/_4\lambda$. Near base capacitance also modifies the matching under some frequency and ground plane conditions.

Fig 6.21 shows a design for a 145MHz helical antenna. With the 9mm diameter shown, the helix acts as a $^3/_4\lambda$. In the original design a sub-miniature plug was used. More appropriate for most applications, a BNC could be used successfully.

CAR-MOUNTING OF VERTICAL ANTENNAS
In view of the very high usage of verticals in mobile applications, there is a very wide variety on the market. There are several ways in which these antennas can be mounted on cars. The best way is to have a permanent mount. While this is the most satisfactory, it does mean putting a special

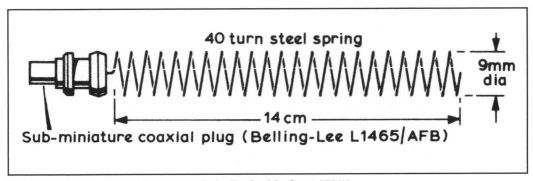

Fig 6.21: Details of the home-made helical whip for 145MHz.

hole in the car bodywork just for the antenna and often this is not acceptable. To overcome this problem, several other mounts are available for cars which do not need any alterations to the car.

One of the most common is a magnetic mount ('mag-mount' for short). This form of mount has a base, about 12 or 15cm in diameter, which includes a strong magnet. This enables the mount to be placed on the metalwork of the car and be held firmly in place. This has the advantage that it can be easily removed when the antenna is not required, or the car is left unattended. When using a magnetic mount, care should be taken to ensure that the rubber base remains free from dirt and grit otherwise the paint-work very soon becomes scratched.

Another method uses an attachment which fits to the gutter along the side of the car roof. Gutter mounts do not require any modifications to the car and they are a little more permanent than the magnetic mount. However, they normally use a connector so that the antenna can be removed. This is very useful for the security point of view and it also allows for antennas to be changed if required, for example if the frequency band is changed.

REFERENCES AND FURTHER READING

[1]   'Novice Notebook: $^5/_8$-wavelength vertical antenna for 70cm', Ian Keyser, G3ROO, *RadCom*, Nov 1994.

[2]   'The VHF J-antenna', Ian Keyser, G3ROO, *RadCom*, Sep 1996.

[3]   'Eurotek: Omnidirectional vertically-polarised antenna for 145 and 435MHz', Bert Veukens, PA0HMV, edited and translated by Erwin David, G4LQI, from an original article in *Electron*, April 1999. *RadCom*, Sep 1999.

[4]   *Radio Communication Handbook* 9th Edition, Ed Mike Dennison, G3XDV, and John Fielding, ZS5JF (RSGB).

[5]   *The VHF / UHF Handbook*, ed Andy Barter, G8ATD, (RSGB).

Chapter 7
Wide-Band Antennas

In this Chapter
- THE DISCONE
- OPERATION
- LOG-PERIODIC ARRAY
- LOG-PERIODIC DESIGN
- LOG-PERIODIC YAGI
- G3FDW 70MHz 8-ELEMENT LOG-PERIODIC YAGI
- THE G3FDW 50MHz 5-ELEMENT LOG-PERIODIC YAGI
- THE G3FDW 144MHz 7-ELEMENT LOG-PERIODIC YAGI
- THE G3FDW 144MHz 10-ELEMENT LOG-PERIODIC YAGI
- THE G3FDW MULTIBAND LOG-PERIODIC YAGI

All the antennas described so far have been able to cover only a comparatively small band of frequencies. For example, Yagis can cover only a single amateur band, and even then they may be optimised for a particular portion of that band. Other antennas such as the verticals may be designed to cover more than one band. However, none described so far has been able to provide continuous coverage over a significant band of frequencies. In fact, most antennas are only be able to operate over frequency ranges that correspond to a few percent of the operating frequency.

Fortunately, some types are able to operate over a very wide band of frequencies. Unlike other antennas which cover a single band, or possibly several bands, their performance remains substantially the same over a range of frequencies covering a span of 2:1 or possibly even more. Commercially, they are used for a variety of different applications. For amateur applications they find uses especially with scanners. As the scanner is able to cover a very wide range of frequencies very quickly, it is not convenient to have a wide range of antennas which have to be switched. The only viable solution is to use a proper wide-band antenna.

THE DISCONE
This must be the most popular type of wide-band antenna used by scanner enthusiasts, as well as for commercial applications and the military. It is almost omnidirectional and it can operate over a frequency range of up to 10:1 in certain instances. In addition to this, it offers a low angle of radiation and reception that is particularly important at VHF and UHF. However, it must be said that the angle of radiation does increase at the top of the frequency range. Despite these advantages, it is only rarely used for amateur transmitting applications. One of the reasons is that its wide bandwidth could lead to the radiation of spurious signals that may not be sufficiently filtered in the transmitter. Also, the SWR will vary over the bandwidth of the antenna, which by its very nature will not be optimised

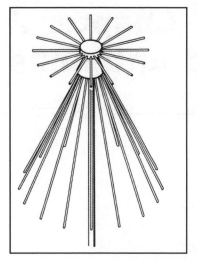

Fig 7.1: A discone antenna.

for a particular band. For those interested in antenna construction, the discone is not the easiest antenna to construct, although it is possible if you have workshop facilities.

The discone derives its name from the distinctive shape, shown in **Fig 7.1**. From this diagram, it can be seen that the antenna basically consists of a disc section and a cone section that are simulated by a number of rods. The disc section is insulated from the cone by a block of material that also acts as a spacer keeping the two sections a fixed distance apart. In fact, this distance is one of the factors that determines the overall frequency range of the antenna.

When designing a discone, the length of the cone elements (length A in **Fig 7.2**) should be a quarter-wavelength at the minimum operating frequency, f. This can be calculated from

$$A(\text{mm}) = \frac{75000}{f(\text{MHz})} \text{,}$$

Having decided upon this, the disc elements should be made to have an overall length, B, of 0.7 of a quarter-wavelength.

$$B(\text{mm}) = \frac{525500}{f(\text{MHz})}$$

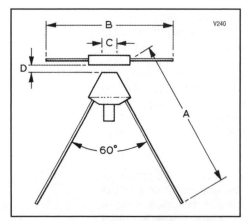

Fig 7.2: Critical dimensions of a discone.

The diameter of the top of the cone (usually about 15mm) is mainly dependent upon the diameter of the coaxial cable being used. The spacing between the cone and the disc should be about a quarter of the inner diameter of the cone, and will generally be about 4mm. Making the minimum diameter of the cone small will increase the upper frequency limit of the antenna.

OPERATION

The actual operation of a discone is quite complicated, but it is possible to visualise it in a simplified qualitative manner. First, the elements which form the disc and cone tend to simulate electrically a complete surface from which the energy is radiated. Although the number of elements used is not critical, it is found that a better simulation of the disc and cone is achieved when more elements are used. However, additional elements will add both to the cost and the wind resistance of the antenna and therefore it is normal to use about six or eight elements.

In operation, energy from the feeder meets the antenna and spreads over the surface of the cone from the apex towards the base until the vertical distance between the point on the cone and the disc is a quarter wavelength. At this point resonance is seen and the energy is radiated.

The radiated signal is vertically polarised as one might expect and the radiation pattern is very similar to that of a vertical dipole. Although some variation is seen over the operating band, particularly at the top, it maintains a very good low angle of radiation over most of the range. Typically, one would expect virtually no change over a frequency range of 5:1 and above this a slight increase in the angle is seen.

From the circuit viewpoint, it is found that the current maximum is at the top of the antenna as might be expected. It is also found that, below the minimum frequency, the antenna presents a very bad mismatch to the feeder. However, once the frequency rises above this point then a good match to 50Ω coax is maintained over virtually the whole of the band.

In view of the difficulties of fabricating the centre insulator most people opt to buy a discone when one is required. A large variety is available from stockists for very reasonable prices

LOG-PERIODIC ARRAY

The log-periodic antenna was originally designed at the University of Illinois in the USA in 1955. Since then, it has found widespread acceptance in military and other commercial applications where a wide-band beam antenna is required, although it is not widely used in amateur circles.

The antenna is directional and is normally capable of operating over a frequency range of about 2:1. It has many similarities to the more familiar Yagi because it exhibits forward gain and has a significant F/B ratio. In addition to this, the radiation pattern stays broadly the same over the whole of the operating band, as do parameters like the radiation resistance and the standing-wave ratio. However it offers less gain for its size than does the more conventional Yagi.

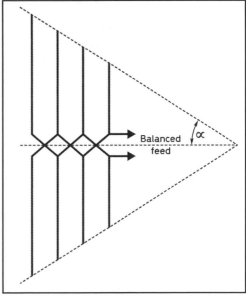

Fig 7.3: A log-periodic array.

Several varieties of log-periodic antenna exist. They include the planar, zig-zag, slot, V and the dipole. The type most used in amateur circles is the dipole or log-periodic dipole array (LPDA). The basic format for the array is shown in **Fig 7.3**. Essentially it consists of a number of dipole elements of sizes that steadily diminish from the back of the beam where the largest element is a half-wavelength at the lowest frequency. The element spacings also decrease towards the front of the array, where the smallest elements are located. In operation, as the frequency changes there is a smooth transition along the array of the elements that form the active region. To ensure that the phasing of the different elements is correct, the feed phase is reversed as shown in the diagram.

The operation of a log-periodic can be explained in a fairly simple qualitative manner. From the diagram it can be seen that the polarity of the feeder is reversed between successive elements. For the sake of the explanation, imagine a signal applied to the antenna somewhere around the middle of its operating range. When the signal meets the first few elements it will be found that they are spaced quite close together in terms of the operating wavelength. This means that the fields from these elements will cancel one another out as the feeder sense is reversed between the elements. Then as the signal progresses down the antenna a point is reached where the feeder reversal and the distance between the elements gives a total phase shift of about 360°. At this point, the effect which is seen is that of two phased dipoles. The region in which this occurs is called the *active region* of the antenna. Although the example of only two dipoles is given, in reality the active region can consist of more elements. The actual number depends upon the angle,α, and a design constant.

The other elements receive little direct power. However, the larger elements are resonant below the operational frequency and appear inductive. Those in front resonate above the operational frequency and are capacitive. These are exactly the same criteria that are found in the Yagi. Accordingly, the element immediately behind the active region acts as a reflector and those in front act as directors. This means that the direction of maximum radiation is towards the feed-point.

The feed impedance and feed arrangements of the log period antenna are also important. The antenna presents a number of difficulties if it is to be fed properly. Its input impedance is dependent upon a number of factors. Fortunately, the overall antenna feed impedance can be determined largely by the impedance of the feeder which connects the elements within the antenna itself. However, the main problem to overcome is that the impedance will vary according to the frequency in use. To a large extent this can be compensated by making the longer elements out of a larger diameter rod. Even so, the final feed impedance does not normally match a convenient 50Ω on its own. It is normal to use some further form of impedance matching. This may be in the form of a stub or even a transformer. The actual method employed will depend to a large degree on the application of the antenna and its frequency range.

In summary, a log-periodic antenna will provide modest levels of gain, typically around 4 to 6dBd, although some designs will give a little more. However only three or four elements are generally active on any given frequency, the remainder remaining passive and not contributing to the operation. Typically SWR levels of better than 1.3:1 can be achieved over an operating frequency range of 2:1 if it is fed via a simple balun. As such it enables wide-band operation to be achieved with some gain and the use of only a single feeder. This is a significant advantage in many applications, although for many amateur uses higher levels of gain are needed, especially at VHF and UHF.

LOG-PERIODIC DESIGN

A log-periodic antenna can be built relatively easily in the form shown in **Fig 7.4**. It should be noted that the element lengths for the highest frequency have been calculated for the elements to be inserted right through the boom, and flush with the far wall. These lengths were calculated from a computer-aided design programme [1]. The two lower frequency antennas have element lengths calculated to butt flush against the element side of the boom. If the elements are to be inserted through the boom on the 21 - 55MHz and the 50 - 150MHz antennas, the boom diameter must be added to the length of each element.

As the supporting booms are also the transmission line between the elements for a log-periodic antenna, they must be supported with a dielectric spacing from the mast of at least twice the boom-to-boom spacing, otherwise discontinuities will be introduced into the feed system. Feed-line connection and the arrangement for the 'infinite balun' is shown in **Fig 7.5**. Any change in boom diameters will necessitate a change in the boom-to-boom spacing to maintain the feed impedance.

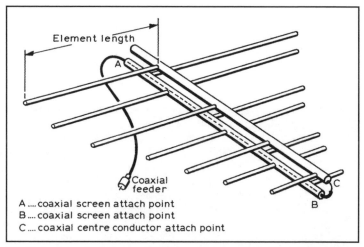

A .... coaxial screen attach point
B .... coaxial screen attach point
C .... coaxial centre conductor attach point

Fig 7.4: A typical log-periodic antenna. Note that the bottom boom is fed from the coaxial outer while the top boom is fed from the centre conductor (courtesy *Ham Radio* – CQ Communications Inc).

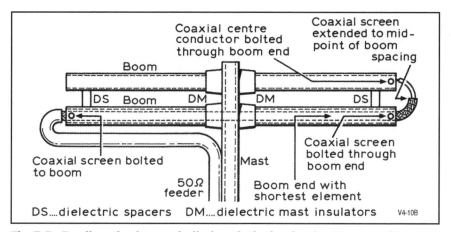

DS....dielectric spacers   DM....dielectric mast insulators   V4-10B

Fig 7.5: Feeding the log-periodic is relatively simple. Remove the outer plastic jacket from the feed-line for the entire length of the boom so that the coaxial outer is permitted to short itself inside the boom as well as making solid electrical connections at either end of the boom. (courtesy *Ham Radio* – CQ Communications Inc).

Ele-ment	21 - 55MHz array			50 - 150MHz array			140 - 450MHx array		
	Length (mm)	Diameter (mm)	Spacing (mm)	Length (mm)	Diameter (mm)	Spacing (mm)	Length (mm)	Diameter (mm)	Spacing (mm)
1	3731	38.1	1050	1602	2.54	630	535	6.7	225
2	3411	31.8	945	1444	2.54	567	479	6.7	202
3	3073	31.8	850	1303	2.54	510	397	6.7	182
4	2770	31.8	765	1175	19.1	459	383	6.7	164
5	2496	31.8	689	1060	19.1	413	341	6.7	148
6	2250	25.4	620	957	19.1	372	304	6.7	133
7	2029	25.4	558	864	19.1	335	271	6.7	119
8	1830	19.1	500	781	12.7	301	241	6.7	108
9	1650	19.1	452	705	12.7	271	215	6.7	97
10	1489	19.1	407	637	12.7	244	190	6.7	87
11	1344	19.1	366	576	12.7	219	169	6.7	78
12	1213	12.7	329	522	9.5	198	149	6.7	70
13	1095	12.7	0	472	9.5	178	131	6.7	63
14				428	9.5	160	115	6.7	57
15				388	9.5	0	101	6.7	52
16							88	6.7	0
Boom	7620	50.8	12.7	5090	38.1	152	1823	38.1	152

Table 7.1: Spacing and dimensions for log-periodic VHF Antennas.

Element	Length (mm)	Diameter (mm)	Spacing (mm)
1	178	2.1	75
2	159	2.1	67
3	133	2.1	61
4	127	2.1	55
5	114	2.1	49
6	101	2.1	44
7	91	2.1	40
8	80	2.1	36
9	72	2.1	32
10	63	2.1	29
11	56	2.1	26
12	50	2.1	23
13	44	2.1	21
14	38	2.1	19
15	34	2.1	17
16	30	2.1	0
Boom	607	12.7	

Table 7.2: Spacing and dimensions for log-periodic UHF Antenna (420 - 1350MHz array).

LOG-PERIODIC YAGI

The log-periodic Yagi (LPY) antenna combines many of the advantages of a log-periodic array with those of the more conventional Yagi concept. The antenna can be visualised in two sections. The first is the log period feed cell, and the second is the Yagi section. This combination provides both a high level of gain and an efficient wide-band feed, all on a short boom. In turn, this means that the antenna has a lower wind resistance and greater strength than a Yagi of similar gain. The drawback is that the antenna is not truly wide-band because the Yagi section is only resonant on a given frequency.

The basic log-periodic cell consists of typically four elements, and the additional gain is provided by adding directors. The log-periodic cell provides some gain in its own right, and placing a director in front of it further increases the forward gain. It is accepted that the addition of a single director gives an increase in gain of around 4dB. This can be compared to the gain achieved when a single director is added to a two-element Yagi. Figures for the maximum gain are 4.5dB for a two-element Yagi and 7dB for a three-element Yagi, an increase of 2.5dB. This means that the log-periodic Yagi gives 1.5dB more gain. This may be attributable to the better illumination of the director by the log-periodic cell. It is also possible to add a reflector behind the log-periodic cell. It is found that this improves the F/B ratio from between 12 and 15dB to around 25dB, but does not give a measurable increase in forward gain

As with a Yagi, the addition of parasitic elements, in this case directors, lowers the feed impedance, although to a lesser extent than in the case of the Yagi. The feed impedance of the log cell is dependent mainly upon the construction and dimensions of feed system itself and also the angle, α, at which the elements reduce in size. Impedance measurements indicate that it is mainly resistive with very little reactance over the operating frequency range.

The feed impedance of most log-periodic designs using open-wire feeder to feed the elements is between 200Ω and 300Ω. This feed impedance can be varied by altering the spacing of the feed wires, or alternatively by changing the spacing of the elements.

G3FDW 70MHz 8-ELEMENT LOG-PERIODIC YAGI

The design for this 8-element antenna (**Fig 7.6**)provides a calculated gain of just over 11dBd. It is robust and has been in use for several years at the designer's home in Cumbria. The weight is below 3kg and its cost was comparable with that of a commercially-made Yagi with similar gain but, of course, the commercial Yagi would not have all the advantages of the log-periodic Yagi.

The feed-point impedance of the antenna itself was measured to be 300Ω. To match this to the coax, a 4:1 coaxial balun (**Fig 7.7**) was used. Not only did this

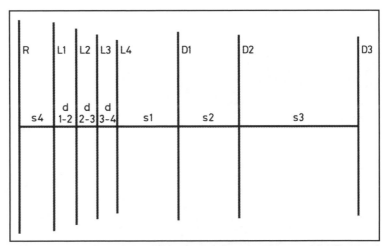

Fig 7.6: Details of the 70MHz 8-element log-periodic Yagi array.

provide the impedance match, but it also provided the balanced-to-unbalanced transformation that is also needed. Final adjustment of the match was effected by altering the log-periodic cell feed-line spacing to give a 1.2:1 SWR at 70.2MHz using 52Ω coax. The feed-line was constructed using 1.6mm wire. This was sufficiently robust and enabled the spacing to be adjusted for matching. It was found that an impedance variation of 2:1 could be achieved by varying the spacing. Additionally, another concern was that flash-over might occur when very small values of spacing were used. It was found that when the spacing was reduced to 3mm, flash-over did not occur with 100W, even in the rain.

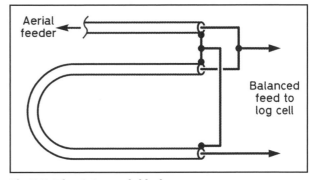

Fig 7.7: The 4:1 coaxial balun.

Connections in box L1 on the log-periodic Yagi.

Once constructed, the performance was assessed. The F/B ratio was found to be 25dB with the close-spaced reflector, and 12dB without it. The half-power beam-width was measured at between 40 and 45° and the forward gain was assessed at between 11 and 12dBd, providing very accurate correlation between the calculated gain and the actual measurements.

The construction of the antenna can be broken down into a number of different steps. First join the two halves of the boom using a 300mm length of 22mm outside diameter tubing and self-tapping screws.

Next, drill all the element locating holes in the boom. Then mount the four feed-cell insulating boxes.

Next, drill two holes in the L1 and L4 boxes and four holes in the L2 and L3 boxes. These should be 19mm apart and accommodate the 1.6mm wire feed-line. The holes are best drilled from the inside of the boxes, so that they have a slight downward tilt to prevent water ingress. Make sure that all the

Connections in boxes L2 and L3.

connecting posts in the insulating boxes are pulled down tight and that they are correctly aligned for the feed-line connections.

Connect the enamelled copper wire feed-line, making the crossover connections in boxes L1, L2, and L3. Connect the coaxial feeder in box L4. All outer braids are soldered together as shown in the photograph and in Fig 7.7.

Connections in box L4, showing feed-line, feeder and balun connections.

Drill and fit the half-elements: L1, L2, L3 and L4, but make them all too long. Then measure and mark the elements L1 and L4. Lay a straight edge between these marks and mark the lengths for L2 and L3. Cut the elements to size. In this way, the correct taper for the log cell is obtained.

Make the director and reflector elements and cut them to length *in situ*. All directors and reflectors are of one continuous length, but the reflector has two 150mm x 6.3mm extensions, each fitted with a single self-tapping screw.

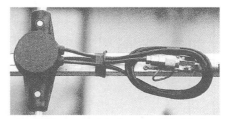

The 4:1 coaxial balun and lightning arrestor.

Element list

L1	2.15m
L2	2.02m
L3	1.90m
L4	1.79m
D1	1.94m
D2	1.89m
D3	1.84m
Rfl	2.20m
d1 - 2	236mm
d2 - 3	222mm
d3 - 4	209mm
s1	641mm
s2	641mm
s3	1.28m
s4	363mm

Table 7.3: Dimensions for the 8-element 70MHz log-periodic Yagi.

Make the 4:1 coaxial balun from exactly 1.41m of UR-47 coax. The connections are shown in Fig 7.7 and the photos of the connecting box. The balun is coiled up and strapped to the boom. The coax feed is via a UHF connector and a lightning arrestor with its earth strap taken to a self tapping screw into the boom. On completion, spray inside each of the dipole boxes with car wax underseal and refit the lids.

Parts list

Quantity	Description
2	Boom 25.4mm-square section, 1.83m lengths
1	Boom coupling tube, 305 x 22.2mm OD
4	Insulating blocks, 25.4mm-square boom to 12.7mm dipole fitting
8	Seamless tube 1.0 m x 12.7mm OD
2	Seamless tube 1.98m x 12.7mm for D1 and D2
2	Seamless tube 1.98m x 9.5mm for D3 and Rfl
2	Seamless tube 152 x 6.3mm secured in each end of the reflector with a self-tapping screw
4	Mounting clips 25.4mm-square boom to 12.7mm element
1	UHF coax fitting with lightning arrestor as illustrated in the photo. As the feed elements are not earthed to the mast, this is a safety precaution.
2	End caps for 25.4mm-square tubing
2	End caps for 9.5mm-OD tubing
2	End caps for 12.7mm-OD tubing
4m	Enamelled copper wire 1.6mm-diameter
3m	UR-47 coax feeder for the balun

Table 7.4: Materials list.

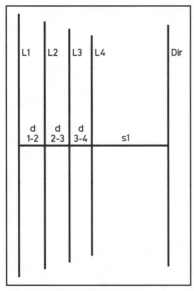

Fig 7.8: The 50MHz 5-element log-periodic Yagi.

THE G3FDW 50MHz 5-ELEMENT LOG-PERIODIC YAGI

The 50MHz version of the antenna is very similar to the 70MHz version (see **Fig 7.8**). The gain was calculated to be 9.36dBd and the total boom length is 1.83m. The construction follows much the same steps as for the 70MHz log-periodic Yagi, though with a few differences. The feed-line uses 2mm enamelled copper wire instead of the 1.6mm wire used on the 70MHz version.

The feed to the log cell uses a short length of thin 70Ω coax, wound in six turns on an RSGB ferrite core to form a choke balun. The coax ends are connected to the feed cell terminals.

The original antenna was built using 25mm outside diameter round tubing for the boom, but a square boom like that used for the 70MHz antenna could also be used. To improve the F/B ratio, L1 is fitted with a 175mm shorting loop.

Element list	
L1	3.00m
L2	2.82m
L3	2.66m
d1 - 2	305mm
d2 - 3	287mm
d3 - 4	270mm
D1	2.75m
s1	902mm
L4	2.51m

Table 7.5: Dimensions for 50MHz log-periodic Yagi.

THE G3FDW 144MHz 7-ELEMENT LOG-PERIODIC YAGI

This antenna is very similar to the previous two. Its gain is calculated to be just over 11dBd and it has a boom length of around 1.5m. The design is for the low end of the 144MHz band and, in fac,t the feed cell was designed for 141MHz to improve the F/B ratio without the need for an additional reflector. The antenna was adjusted to give an SWR of 1.1:1 at 144.3MHz but, despite this, it still provided an SWR of only 1.5:1 at 145.5MHz, making it suitable for use anywhere in the band.

The connections to L1, L2, and L3 from the 1.6mm feed wire are made using small solder tags attached to each element using small self-tapping screws, and all connections are soldered *in situ* to ensure that the wiring exactly fits in.

144MHz 7-element log-periodic Yagi.

THE G3FDW 144MHz 10-ELEMENT LOG-PERIODIC YAGI

This antenna was developed from the original 7-element version. It provides extra gain that can be very useful, especially during contests. The boom length was doubled, enabling three further directors to be added. This changed the feed impedance of the antenna and as a result the original 4:1 balun became redundant. Measurements showed the feed impedance of the antenna to be 45Ω with very little reactive component. The perfect match was provided by slightly repositioning director 3 (D3) to give the dimensions described in **Fig 7.9**.

Close-up of the 144MHz log cell feed-line.

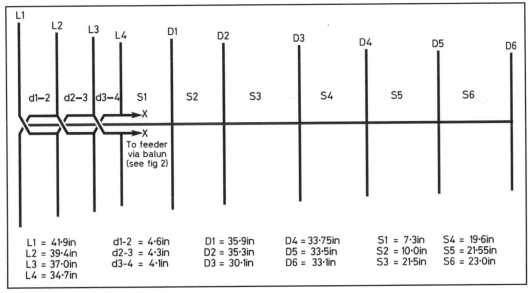

L1 = 41·9in
L2 = 39·4in
L3 = 37·0in
L4 = 34·7in

d1-2 = 4·6in
d2-3 = 4·3in
d3-4 = 4·1in

D1 = 35·9in
D2 = 35·3in
D3 = 30·1in

D4 = 33·75in
D5 = 33·5in
D6 = 33·1in

S1 = 7·3in
S2 = 10·0in
S3 = 21·5in

S4 = 19·6in
S5 = 21·55in
S6 = 23·0in

Fig 7.9: The 10-element log-periodic Yagi.

The antenna is connected to the feeder using an untuned balun (**Fig 7.10**), purely to provide the balanced-to-unbalanced transformation with no impedance change. Using this, a very good match was achieved over the DX portion of the 2m band.

The LPY was installed on a mast nearly 8m high. Tests with other stations who were able to give some indication of the polar diagram showed that the F/B ratio was around 15 to 20dB with the minor lobes better than 25dB down.

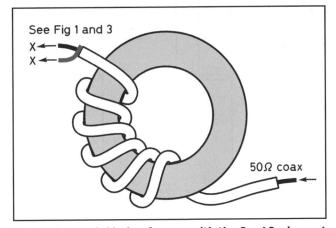

See Fig 1 and 3

X
X

50Ω coax

Fig 7.10: Coaxial balun for use with the 2m 10-element log-periodic Yagi.

Components list for the 10-element Yagi

Boom 3.2m of 25.4mm-diameter aluminium tube
Elements   all 9.5 mm-diam seamless tube
4 dipole fittings   Metal element fittings, 9.5 to 25.4mm-diam required

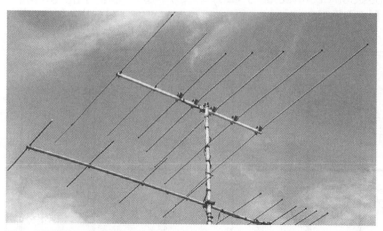

The G3FDW multiband and 10-element 2m log-periodic Yagi arrays.

THE G3FDW MULTIBAND LOG-PERIODIC YAGI

As the log-periodic cell is capable of operating over a wide frequency range, the idea of this antenna is to provide operation on several VHF bands. By making the log cell operate over a sufficiently wide frequency range, more than one band can be covered, and additional gain provided by directors for each of the bands. The antenna was originally intended for operation on 50MHz and 70MHz. The gain was estimated to be 7 to 8dBd, and the F/B ratio was found to be between 10 and 12dB.

The final design shown in **Fig 7.11** uses five elements in the log-periodic cell and a further two elements as directors, one for each of the two bands. Once the feed cell was constructed, it was tested by measuring the feed impedance over the design bandwidth of 50 to 70MHz. Over this range, the impedance was substantially flat with the value varying over the range (90 ± 25)Ω. The cell actually showed a typical band-pass characteristic with large changes in impedance outside the design range.

The two directors were fitted and the SWR measured with the beam

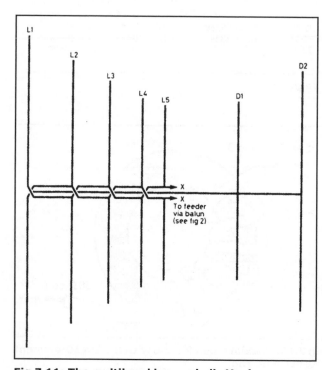

Fig 7.11: The multiband log-periodic Yagi.

mounted on a pole with the antenna a short distance from the ground, and beamed vertically. The SWR improved over the log cell itself as the directors lowered the impedance. Adjusting the spacing of the log cell feeder made a further improvement. The feeder spacing between L1 to L2 and L2 to L3 affected the 6m feed impedance while the spacing of the feeder between L3 to L4 and L4 to L5 determined the 4m feed impedance.

It was found that the antenna would also operate very satisfactorily on 144MHz. This is because the 12.7mm-diameter 6m elements of the cell are three half-wavelengths long and present a low impedance when fed in the centre. Unfortunately, the arrangement produced two narrow lobes at an angle of about 40° either side of the main line of the boom. The beam splitting could be corrected by angling the log cell elements to align with the lobes to produce a single main lobe. This would give an additional 3dB gain compared to a log cell with half-wavelength elements. Such an arrangement could be considered as a series of V-beams fed out-of-phase. Work carried out on this by K4EWG [3] indicated the gain for this array would be in the region of 10dB. Although this was investigated, it was not included in the final design because this configuration would be mechanically much weaker and would require bracing. This would have defeated one of the main objectives of the design of the beam.

The construction of the beam is the same as for the other log-periodic Yagis above. It is worth noting that the 12.7mm-diameter elements L2 and L4 are resonant on 50.2MHz and 70.2MHz, respectively.

Element list

Boom	1.828m
L1	3.390m
L2	2.838m
L3	2.376m
L4	1.988m
L5	1.664m
d1 - 2	339mm
d2 - 3	284mm
d3 - 4	237mm
d4 - 5	199mm
D1	1.955m
D2	2.775m
s1	311mm
s2	412mm

Table 7.6: Dimensions for the multiband log-periodic Yagi.

Parts list

Boom	25.4mm-square section x 1.83m (72in)
L1 to L5	12.7mm seamless tube
5 insulated dipole fittings	12.7mm to 25.4mm-square
D1, D2	9.5mm seamless tube
2 mounting clips	9.5mm to 25.4mm-square
1.6 mm enamelled wire	as required

Table 7.7: Materials for the multiband log-periodic Yagi.

REFERENCES AND FURTHER READING

[1]   'Log-periodic antennas', W3DUQ, *Ham Radio*, Aug 1970.

[2]   'The VHF log-periodic Yagi', Mike Gibbins, G3FDW, *RadCom*, Jul 1994.

[3]   'More on G3FDW log-periodic Yagis', Mike Gibbins, G3FDW, *RadCom*, Dec 1995

[4]   'The K4EWG log-periodic array', Peter D Rhodes, *The ARRL Antenna Compendium*, <u>3</u> p118.

[5]   *The VHF / UHF Handbook*, ed Andy Barter, G8ATD, RSGB.

Chapter 8
Microwave Antennas

In this Chapter
- PARABOLIC REFLECTOR
- HORN ANTENNA

There are several antennas that tend to be used only on microwave frequencies. This can be for a variety of reasons ranging from the size required to other factors including the type of feed they might use. Two forms of antenna that fall into this category are the parabolic reflector or dish antenna and the second is the horn antenna.

PARABOLIC REFLECTOR
The parabolic reflector or dish antenna has been used far more widely in recent years with advent of domestic satellite television (TV). However, the dish antenna finds uses in many radio and wireless applications at frequencies usually above about 1GHz where very high levels of RF antenna gain are required along with narrow beam-widths. In many professional applications these parabolic reflectors or dish antennas are used for satellite communications as well as for radio astronomy and it is used in many microwave links, often being seen on radio relay towers and mobile phone antenna masts. In all these applications, very high levels of gain are required to receive the incoming signals that are often at a very low level. For transmitting, this type of RF antenna design is able to concentrate the available radiated power into a narrow beam-width, ensuring all the available power is radiated in the required direction.

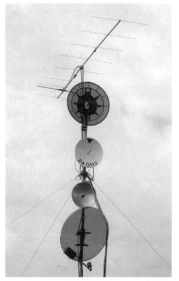

An array of parabolic reflectors topped by a Yagi.

Parabolic Reflector Basics
This RF antenna consists of a radiating system that is used to illuminate a reflector curved in the form of a parabola. This shape enables a very accurate beam to be obtained. The antenna exists in two basic forms. The first is called the *focal-feed reflector*, where the source of radiation is placed at the focal point of the parabola and this is used to illuminate the reflector. **Fig 8.1** illustrates this.

An alternative form of feeding the RF antenna design is known as a *Cassegrain reflector* system. Here, the radiation is fed through the centre of the reflector towards a hyperbolic reflector which reflects the

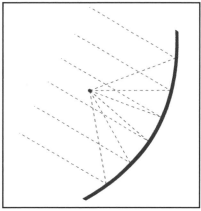

Fig 8.1: The basic use of a focal-feed parabolic reflector antenna.

radiation back to the parabolic reflector. In this way, it is possible to control the radiation more accurately.

The gain is a function of the diameter of the reflecting surface, the surface accuracy, and the quality of the illumination from the radiator. Despite these factors, it is possible to estimate the gain of the antenna which can be deduced from the following formula

$$G = 10.\log\left(k\left(\frac{\pi D}{\lambda}\right)^2\right) \text{, where}$$

G is the gain over an isotropic source;
k is the efficiency factor, which is generally about 50%;
D is the diameter of the parabolic reflector in metres;
λ is the wavelength of the signal in metres.

From this it can be seen that very large gains can be achieved if sufficiently large reflectors are used. However, when the antenna has a very large gain, the beam-width is also very small and the antenna requires very careful control of its position. In professional systems, electrical servos are used to provide very precise positioning.

To provide the optimum illumination of the reflecting surface, the level of illumination should be greater in the centre than at the sides. It can be shown that the optimum situation occurs when the centre is around 10 - 11dB greater than the illumination at the edge. Lower levels of edge illumination result in lower levels of side lobes. The ratio of the focal length, f, to the diameter, D, is useful for this. The f/D ratio is often quoted on designs and it is a little akin to the 'aperture' of an optical lens.

The reflecting surface of the antenna forms a major part of the whole system. In many respects it is not as critical as may be thought at first. Often, a wire mesh may be used. Provided that the pitch of the mesh is small compared to a wavelength, it will be seen as a continuous surface by the radio signals. If a mesh is used, the wind resistance will be reduced, and this provides significant advantages.

One of the chief requirements of the antenna is to ensure that the feed system matches the geometry of the dish itself. The first requirement is to ensure that the feed-point is placed at the focal point of the reflector. This can be calculated from the formula

$$f = \frac{D^2}{16c} \text{, where}$$

f is the distance of the focal point from the reflector;
D is the diameter of the reflector;
c is the depth of the dish.

Dimensions must all be consistent, eg all in centimetres, or all in metres, etc.

There are two basic forms of feed arrangement that can be used for parabolic reflectors. These are the Cassegrain system and the focal-feed arrangement. Of these the focal-feed is the most widely used, and then an offset version of the focal-feed, known as the offset-feed is also used as it provides a number of advantages.

Cassegrain feed system

The Cassegrain feed system, although requiring a second reflecting surface, has the advantage that the overall length of the dish antenna between the two reflectors is shorter than the length between the radiating element and the parabolic reflector. This is because there is a reflection in the focusing of the signal which shortens the physical length. This can be an advantage in some systems.

Focal-feed system

As the name suggests the focal-feed arrangement uses a system where the radiating element is placed at the primary focal point of the reflecting surface, and the radiating element may be a simple dipole or a waveguide horn antenna. The energy from the radiating element is arranged so that it illuminates the reflecting surface. Once the energy is reflected, it leaves the antenna system in a narrow beam. As a result, considerable levels of gain can be achieved.

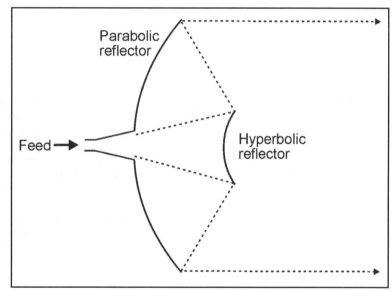

Achieving this is not always easy because it is dependent upon the radiator that is used. For lower frequencies, a dipole element is often

Fig 8.2: Diagram of a focal-feed parabolic reflector or dish antenna with a Cassegrain feed.

employed whereas, at higher frequencies, a circular waveguide may be used. In fact, the circular waveguide provides one of the optimum sources of illumination.

Offset-feed

An offset-fed dish antenna is essentially a form of focal-feed system, but has been modified to enable it to be implemented more easily and effectively. It has a reflector that is a section of a normal parabolic reflector, as shown in **Fig 8.3**. If the section does not include the centre of the dish, then none of the radiated beam is blocked by the feed and support structure. For small dishes, feed blockage in an axial-feed dish causes a

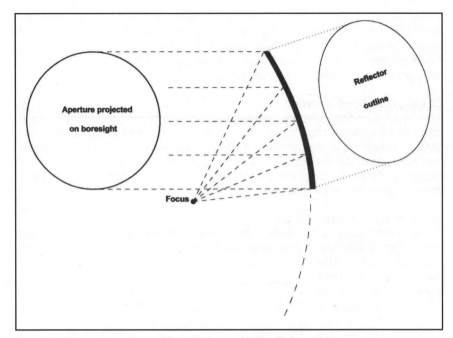

Fig.8.3: Geometry of an offset-fed parabolic dish antenna.

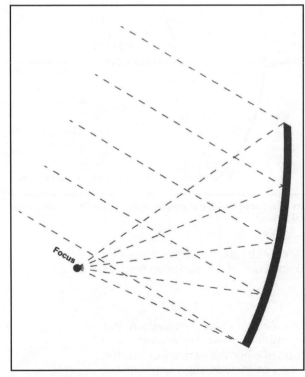

Fig 8.4: Offset-fed parabolic dish antenna aimed at a satellite.

significant loss in efficiency. Thus, we might expect an offset-fed dish to have higher efficiency than a conventional dish of the same aperture. Its use is illustrated in **Fig 8.4**.

In addition to higher efficiency, an offset-fed dish has another advantage for satellite reception. The dish in **Fig 8.4**, aimed upward toward a satellite, has its feed pointing toward the sky.

A conventional dish would have the feed above it, pointing toward the ground, as was shown in Fig 8.1. Any spillover from the feed pattern of the conventional dish would receive noise from the warm earth, while spillover from the offset dish would receive less noise from the cool sky. Since a modern low-noise receiver has a noise temperature much lower than the earth, the conventional dish will be noisier. This is the G/T value; the offset dish offers higher gain, G, since the efficiency is higher, plus reduced noise temperature, T, so the G/T ratio is improved. The higher gain means more signals may be received from a source, and the lower noise temperature means that less noise accompanies it, so a higher G/T offers a higher signal-to-noise ratio

Offset-fed parabolic dish

The spread of consumer satellite TV means that good offset-fed dishes can be obtained easily and for reasonable prices. These can be found in a variety of places, but a very good source is Ebay and are known as TVRO (TV Receive Only) or DSS (Digital Satellite System) antennas with sizes from 45cm (18in); they can offer excellent performance at least up to 10GHz.

The design, although a little more complicated to implement than some others included in this book, provides some real scope for experimentation and for the utilisation of commercial products as a basis for the construction. The offset-fed dish design uses an 18in RCA DSS dish, although a Sky dish could also be used.

The geometry of an offset-fed dish antenna is a bit more complicated than a conventional dish antenna, but the measurements needed to use one are straightforward. It is necessary to determine the tilt angle of the reflector first, then do some curve fitting calculations for the dish surface, calculate the focal length, and finally determine the focal point in relation to the offset reflector.

One common type of offset parabolic reflector has an oval shape, with a long axis from top to bottom and a shorter axis from side to side. However, in the beam of this antenna, looking down the boresight, it would appear to be circular, with the feed at the bottom. Tilt the top of the reflector forward, until it appears circular from a distance, and it will be in the correct orientation to operate with the beam on the horizon. The tilt can be determined much more accurately with a simple calculation -

$$\textit{Tilt angle} \text{ (from horizontal) } = \sin^{-1} \frac{\textit{short axis}}{\textit{long axis}} \text{ ;}$$

For the RCA 18in dish, the short axis is 460mm (about 18in) and the long axis is 500mm. Therefore, the tilt angle = $\sin^{-1}$ *(460/500)* = 66.9° above horizontal. At 10GHz, one millimetre is sufficiently accurate for most dish dimensions, so using millimetres for calculations eliminates a lot of tedious decimals.

If the offset-fed reflector is not oval, we can still use the same calculation by placing it on the ground with the reflecting surface upward and filling it with water. The surface of the water in the dish should be an oval just touching the top and bottom rims, the other axis of the oval of water is the shorter axis.

The other dimension we need is location and depth of the deepest point in the dish. The deepest point is probably not at the centre, but somewhere along the long (major) axis. Using a straight-edge across the rim for an oval dish, or the water depth for other shapes, locate the deepest point and measure its depth and distance from the bottom edge on the major axis.

For the RCA dish, the deepest point is 43mm at 228mm from the bottom edge on the major axis.

When the dish is tilted forward to 66.9° above horizontal, the translated coordinates describe the curve of the major axis by three points: 0, 0mm (bottom edge); 49.8, 226.6mm (deepest point); 196, 460mm (top edge).

If the bottom edge is assumed not to be at the axial centre of a full parabola of rotation (the equivalent conventional dish of which the offset-fed dish is a section), but rather is offset from the centre by an amount x_0, y_0, all three points must fit the equation

$$4 \cdot f \cdot (x + x_0) = (y + y_0)^2 .$$

The unknowns are x_0, and y_0, and f, the focal length. Using these gives three equations and three unknowns, a readily soluble 3 x 3 matrix (actually, the 0,0 point allows reduction to a 2 x 2 matrix, even easier, followed by a simple calculation for x_0 and y_0). Version 2 of the HDL_ANT program [4] will do the calculations.

For the RCA dish, the answers are
f = 282.8mm or 11.13in;
x_0 = 0.1mm behind bottom edge;
y_0 = 11mm below bottom edge, so the feed does not block the aperture at all.

However, the bottom edge of the dish should be at the centre of the full parabola, so that x_0 = 0 and y_0 = 0. Repeating the calculations above with slightly different till angles until x_0 = 0 and y_0 = 0; for the RCA dish, the new tilt angle is 68.3° a small change from the original estimate of 66.9°. The focal length is then calculated to be 291mm. Version 3 of the HDL_ANT program will do the improved calculations.

The calculations show the focal length of the dish to be 282.8mm. If it were a full parabola rather than just an offset-fed section, the diameter would be 929mm for an f/D = 0.31. However, a feed horn need only illuminate the smaller angle of the offset-fed section, a subtended angle of about 78°. This subtended angle is the same as that for a conventional dish with an f/D of 0.69, so a feed horn designed for a 0.69 f/D conventional dish should be suitable. The G3RPE graph for rectangular feed horns and the HDL_ANT computer program were used to design suitable rectangular horns, then two of different lengths were made from flashing copper. The HDL_ANT program includes an approximation to G3RPE's curves so that the program can design feed horns for both offset-fed and conventional dishes as well as generating templates for constructing them.

Since the actual reflector geometry has an f/D of 0.31, the focal distance should be quite critical. This dimension is the most critical for dish antenna performance, even more critical for reflectors with smaller *f/D*, so the phase centre of the feed should be positioned within a quarter-wavelength of the focal point. The RCA dish must be tilted forward to an angle of 67.9° from horizontal for terrestrial operation, with the beam on the horizon. In this orientation, the focal point is level with the lower rim of the dish, so that most of the feed horn and all of the feed mounting structure are out of the beam. To locate the focus accurately, the distance to both the top and bottom of the rim was calculated and a knot tied in a piece of string taped to the rim so that the knot was at the focus when the string is pulled taut (see photo). Then a sliding plywood holder for the feed horn was made and taped it in place then adjusted so that the knot in the string was at the phase centre of the horn (see photo). Materials are not critical when they are not in the antenna beam.

The aim of the feed horn needs to be determined. On a conventional dish it is obvious that it is at the centre. However, an offset-feed is much closer to one edge of the dish than the other. Fortunately, it is possible to show that small variations in aiming strategy have little effect, so aiming at the centre of the reflector is close enough.

Tests undertaken on the antenna by W1RIL, WB1FKF, N1BAQ, and N1BWT showed that the RCA dish with a simple rectangular feed horn measured 63% efficiency at 10GHz, significantly higher than *ever* measured on an 18in conventional dish. Varying the focal distance showed that the calculations were correct and that this dimension is critical.

HORN ANTENNA

The horn antenna gains its name from its appearance (**Fig 8.5**) and finds a number of applications in amateur radio microwave systems where it is normally used in conjunction with waveguide feeds. The waveguide can be considered to be opened-out or flared, launching the signal towards the receiving antenna.

Horn antennas are often used as gain standards, and as feeds for dish antennas, as well as being used as RF antennas in their own right. One particular use of horn antennas themselves is for short-range radar systems, such as those used for automotive speed enforcement.

Using a knot tied in a piece of string to place the feed horn accurately at the focus of an offset-fed dish antenna.

Using a plywood holder to position the feed horn for an offset-fed dish.

When used as part of a parabolic reflector, the horn is orientated towards the reflector surface, and is able to give a reasonably even illumination of the surface without allowing radiation to miss the reflector. In this way, it is able to maximise the efficiency of the overall antenna. The use of the horn antenna also minimises the spurious responses of the parabolic reflector antenna to signals that are not in the main lobe.

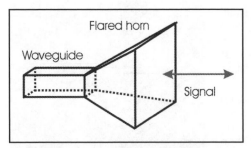

Fig 8.5: The horn antenna is used for many microwave communications applications.

Basic horn antenna concept

The horn antenna may be considered as an RF transformer or impedance match between the waveguide feeder and free space, which has an impedance of 377Ω. By having a tapered or 'flared' end to the waveguide, the horn antenna is formed and this enables the impedance to be matched. Although the waveguide will radiate without a horn antenna, the horn provides a far more efficient match.

In addition to the improved match provided by the horn antenna, it also helps suppress signals travelling in the waveguide in unwanted modes.

However, the main advantages of the horn antenna are that it provides a significant level of directivity and gain which is maintained over a wide bandwidth. For greater levels of gain, the horn antenna should have a large aperture. Also, to achieve the maximum gain for a given aperture size, the taper should be long so that the phase of the wavefront is as nearly constant as possible across the aperture. However, there comes a point where to provide even small increases in gain, the increase in length becomes too large to make it sensible. Thus gain levels are a balance between aperture size and length. However, gain levels for a horn antenna may be up to 20dB in some instances.

A typical horn antenna mounted on a mast.

For horns which are shorter than optimum for a given aperture, the field near the edge lags in relation to the field along the centre line of the horn and causes a loss in gain. For very short horns, this leads to the production of large minor lobes in the radiation pattern. Such short horns can, however, be used quite effectively as feeds for a dish

It is easy to calculate the gain of a horn antenna. It can simply be calculated from the formula

$$Gain = 2.\pi.A.B / \lambda^2 ,$$

where *A* and *B* are the dimensions of the two sides of the horn measured in metres, and λ is the wavelength in metres. Other parameters are illustrated in **Fig 8.6**.

Horn antenna types

There are two basic types of horn antenna: pyramid and conical. The pyramid horns, as the name suggests are rectangular, whereas the corrugated ones are usually circular. The corrugated horn provides a pattern that is nearly symmetrical, with the E- and H-plane beam-widths being nearly the same. Additionally, it is possible to control the side lobes better with a conical or corrugated horn antenna.

Horn antenna for 10GHz

Large pyramidal horns can be an attractive form of antenna for use at 10GHz and above. They are simple to design, tolerant of

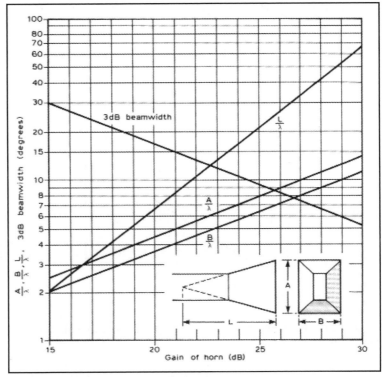

Figure 8.6 Horn antenna design chart.

dimensional inaccuracies during construction and need no adjustment. Additionally, their gains can be predicted within 1dB or so (by simple measurement of the size of the aperture and length) which makes them useful for both the initial checking of the performance of systems and as references against which other antennas can be judged. Their main disadvantage is that they are bulky compared with other antennas having the same gain.

The diagram of a large horn is shown in **Fig 8.7**. As it is a long horn antenna, the emerging wave is nearly planar and the gain of the horn is close to the theoretical value that can be calculated from the equation above. The dimensions for an optimum horn for 10GHz can be calculated from the information given in Fig 8.6 and, for a 20dB horn, are typically: A = 5.19in (132mm); B = 4.25in (108mm); L = 7.67in (195mm).

There is, inevitably, a trade-off between gain and physical size of the horn. At 10GHz, this is in the region of 20dB or perhaps slightly higher. Beyond this point, it is better to use a small dish. For instance, a 27dB horn at 10GHz would have an aperture of 11.8in (300mm) by 8.3in (210mm) and a length of 40.1in (l019mm) compared with a focal-plane

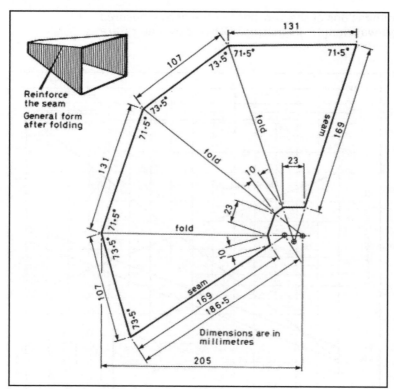

Fig 8.7: Dimensional template for a single-piece-construction 20dB 10GHz horn antenna.

dish that would be 12in (305mm) in diameter and have a length of 3in (76mm) for the same gain.

Horns are usually fabricated from solid sheet metal such as brass, copper or tinplate. There is no reason why they should not be made from perforated or expanded metal mesh, provided that the size and spacing of the holes is kept below about A/10. Construction is simplified if the thickness of the sheet metal is close to the wall thickness of WG16, ie 0.05in or approximately 1.3mm. This simplifies construction of the transition from the waveguide into the horn. The geometry of the horn is not quite as simple as appears at first sight, since it involves a taper from an aspect ratio of about 1:0.8 at the aperture to approximately 2:1 at the waveguide transition. For a superficially rectangular object, a horn contains few right angles, as shown in Fig 8.7 an approximately quarter-scale template for a nominal 20dB horn at 10GHz. If the constructor opts to use the one piece cut and fold method suggested by this figure, it is strongly recommended that a full sized template be drafted on stiff card that can be lightly scored to facilitate bending to final form. This will give the opportunity to correct errors in measurement before transfer to sheet metal and to prove to the constructor that, on folding, a pyramidal horn is formed!

The sheet is best sawn (or guillotined) rather than cut with tin snips, so that the metal remains flat and undistorted. If the constructor has difficulty in folding sheet metal, the horn can be made in two or more pieces, although this will introduce more soldered seams which may need jigging during assembly and also strengthening by means of externally-soldered angle pieces running along the length of each seam. Alternative methods of construction are suggested in **Fig 8.8**.

It is worth paying attention to the transition point that should present a smooth, step-less profile. The junction should also be mechanically strong, since this is the point where the mechanical stresses are greatest. For all but the smallest horns, some form of strengthening is necessary. One simple method of mounting is to take a short length of Old English (OE) waveguide, which has internal dimensions matching the external dimensions of WG16, and slitting each corner for about half the length of the piece. The sides can then be bent out (flared) to suit the angles of the horn and soldered in place after carefully positioning the OE guide over the WG16 and inserting the horn in the flares. One single soldering operation will then fix both in place. After soldering, any excess solder appearing inside the waveguide or throat of the horn should be carefully removed by filing or scraping. The whole assembly can be given a protective coat of paint.

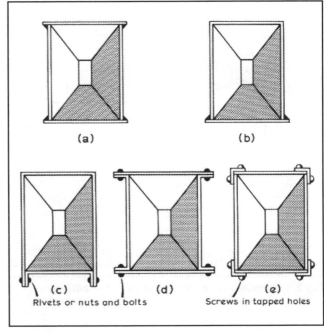

Fig 8.8: Alternative construction methods for horn antennas.

An alternative method would be to omit the WG16 section and to mount the horn directly into a modified WG16 flange. In this case the thickness of the horn material should be a close match with that of WG16 wall thickness and the flange modified by filing a taper of suitable profile into the flange.

Whichever method of fabrication and assembly is used, good metallic contact at the corners is essential. Soldered joints are very satisfactory provided that the amount of solder in the horn is minimised. If sections of the horn are bolted or riveted together, it is essential that many, close-spaced bolts or rivets are used to ensure good contact. Spacing between adjacent fixing points should be less than a wavelength, ie less than 30mm.

24GHz Horn Antenna
A 24GHz horn is a very easy antenna to construct, as its dimensions are not critical and it will provide a good match without any tuning. The dimensions for optimum gain horns of various gains (at 24GHz) are shown and the actual dimensions are given in **Fig 8.9**. Above 25dB, the horn becomes very long and unwieldy and it becomes more practical to use a parabolic reflector or dish.

Suitable materials are PCB material, brass or copper sheet, or tin plate. If PCB material is used, the doubled-sided type will enable the joins to be soldered both inside and out for extra strength. An ideal source of tin plate is an empty oil can.

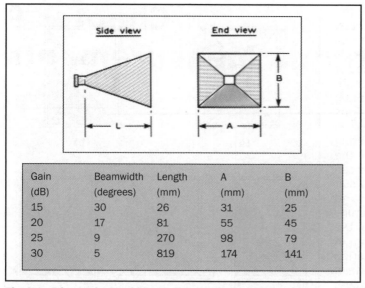

Gain	Beamwidth	Length	A	B
(dB)	(degrees)	(mm)	(mm)	(mm)
15	30	26	31	25
20	17	81	55	45
25	9	270	98	79
30	5	819	174	141

Fig 8.9: Dimensions of horn antenna for 24GHz.

The transition from the guide to the horn should be smooth, Use either a butt joint, or file the waveguide walls to a sharp edge as shown in **Fig 8.10**. The material should be cut to size and soldered together and onto a section of waveguide.

Alternatively, the horn may be coupled directly to the inside of the flange. In this case, the material should be the same thickness as the waveguide would be, and it is bent as it enters the flange, or the flange may be filed to be part of the taper as in **Fig 8.11**.

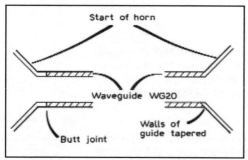

Fig 8.10: Joining a 24GHz horn directly to a waveguide.

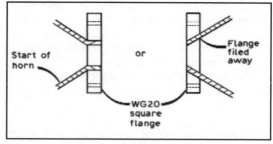

Fig 8.11: Joining a 24GHz horn directly to a flange.

REFERENCES AND FURTHER READING

[1] *The International Microwave Handbook*, ed Andy Barter, G8ATD, RSGB 2008.

[2] *RSGB Radio Communication Handbook* 9th Edn, RSGB 2007.

[3] *The W1GHZ Microwave Antenna Book*, Paul Wade.

[4] HDL_ANT version 3b4 can be downloaded from www.w1ghz.org/software/hdl3b4.zip

[5] The UK Microwave website www.microwavers.org

[6] Pictures courtesy of G4WGE

In this Chapter
- STANDING-WAVE RATIO METERS
- SIMPLE VSWR BRIDGE
- DIP METER
- NOISE BRIDGES

Although choice, construction and installation of an antenna system are very important, like any other area of radio and electronics, it is often necessary to test an antenna. This may be necessary during installation to make sure that it is ready for use. It may be a maintenance test some time after it has been installed to make sure it is still operating correctly. Sometimes, a fault may occur on an antenna and it may be necessary to find out what has failed so that the antenna system can be fixed. There are many tests that can be undertaken and a variety of items of test equipment can be used.

Ordinary test meters can only perform the basic continuity and insulation tests on antennas. Fortunately, some items of antenna test equipment can be improvised or built very easily. However, those who enjoy a lot of experimenting with antennas may choose to invest in more equipment to ensure that the antennas are performing to their best potential. Even so, some items like SWR meters are invaluable and found in virtually every transmitting station.

STANDING-WAVE RATIO METERS
An instrument that can be used to help assess the performance of an antenna is a Standing-Wave Ratio (SWR) meter. By monitoring the standing-wave ratio on a feeder, a very good view of the performance of an antenna system can be gained.

In view of the fact that it needs a certain amount of power to drive it, it is generally used in conjunction with a transmitter. It measures the amount of power travelling down the feeder away from the source and compares it with any reflected power. From this it is able to give a reading of the SWR that exists in the feeder.

If the SWR is high, damage can result to the output devices of the transmitter. To prevent this happening most transmitters today are fitted with circuitry that detects high levels of reflected power and reduces the output to a level where no damage will be caused. The obvious consequence of this is that as the output falls, so does the radiated signal. Another problem occurs because there will be points where the current and voltage reach very high levels. If the transmitter is running at a high power, the current can become sufficiently high to cause local heating.

Alternatively, at the voltage peaks there is the possibility that the dielectric can break down. Both of these possibilities can damage the feeder. In addition to this, a high SWR can mean that there is an imbalance on the feeder and this can lead to radiation from the feeder and a distortion of the antenna radiation pattern. Accordingly, it is necessary to ensure that the SWR is kept to a minimum and, as a result, a knowledge of the SWR in the feeder is very important.

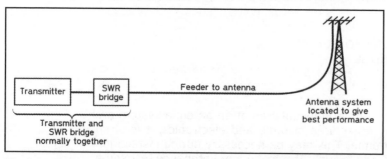

Fig 9.1: The position of an SWR meter in an antenna system.

An SWR bridge is fitted into the feeder as shown in **Fig 9.1**. It is located at the transmitter end of the feeder. It is very convenient because it can be left in circuit all the time. This is useful because it means that many major antenna problems can be detected very quickly. In addition to this, the bandwidth of any antenna system is limited and the SWR will rise either side of the centre frequency. If a transmitter is likely to be used on a number of frequencies then it is necessary to know what the SWR is on the new frequency before applying full power.

While an indication of the SWR at the transmitter end of the feeder is very useful, it does not give a complete picture about the operation of the antenna. There are several reasons for this. One is that a poor feeder can hide a high level of SWR. This is because any feeder has a certain amount of loss, and this will attenuate the power travelling towards the antenna as well as any power that is reflected back. Both of these effects will reduce the amount of reflected power seen by the meter, making the SWR reading seem better than it really is. In fact the higher the level of attenuation in the feeder the better the SWR will seem. Thus, it is quite possible for an antenna to reflect a large proportion of its power, but seem to be operating quite satisfactorily if the feeder loss is high. Even a length of feeder as short as 10λ can make the feeder appear like a good load regardless of the termination. To illustrate the point, many people have used a large reel of coax as a good load. However, when doing this, beware of overheating the cable if the power is to be applied for any length of time and the coax is to be kept on the reel.

There are many meters available for measuring the standing-wave ratio on a feeder or transmission line. Most meters today use directional power sensors, but some take advantage of the fact that voltage on a line consists of two components travelling in opposite directions and give an indication of the voltage standing-wave ratio (VSWR). The forward power is represented by one voltage, and the reflected power by another voltage. It is possible for a bridge circuit to separate the two different voltages and this can enable the standing-wave ratio, or more correctly the voltage standing-wave ratio to be determined. These bridges are frequently called reflectometers. A good range of SWR meters is available from stockists. It is advisable for stations to have an SWR meter that can be used to monitor the level of reflected power.

Low-cost reflectometers that do not have a wattmeter calibration are not particularly reliable for accurate measurements of standing-wave ratio. Fortunately, they are still useful because antennas are adjusted to give the minimum standing-wave ratio. Accordingly, accurate measurements are not required, and only a relative measurement is needed. These devices are often frequency-sensitive, with the meter response rising with frequency.

Many meters these days use a directional power sensor and can be used for power measurement as well. Even so, care should be taken when interpreting their readings as power is always difficult to measure accurately.

SIMPLE VSWR BRIDGE

While in-line SWR meters are widely used, some designs can be used for off-line measurements as well. Most of the measurements that are likely to be made are on the antenna itself or on a feed system. This unit is equally applicable to the measurement of input impedance of an amplifier, and enables measurements to be made that could not be performed with one of the more common meters.

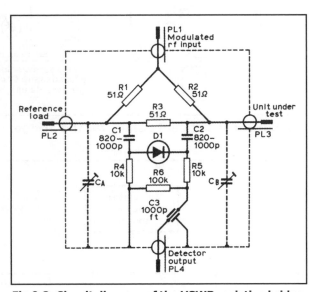

The home-constructed bridge (**Fig 9.2**) can be built without difficulty but, for best performance, care in detail is needed, notably in the choice of the matched resistors R1 and R2. As far as possible their installation should be identical in respect of the lead length that should be kept to a minimum

Fig 9.2: Circuit diagram of the VSWR resistive bridge.

anyway, and their location, particularly in respect of the ground plane and connections. In this way any spurious reactance is balanced out.

The circuit diagram is shown in Fig 9.2, and two methods of construction are detailed in **Fig 9.3**. Both are built into a small diecast boxes. In the first method, the connectors are attached to the sides of the box and the circuit components fitted to single-sided, copper-clad, glass-fibre printed-circuit board. The board is positioned so that it is at the level of the insulation projecting from the BNC connectors. In this way the important resistors, R1, R2, and R3 rest on the copper ground-plane when they are soldered in position. Stand-off insulators can be used for the junction of the components to make the job neater although this is not essential.

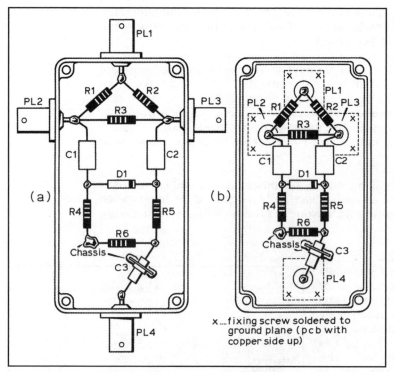

x....fixing screw soldered to ground plane (pcb with copper side up)

Fig 9.3: Constructional details for the bridge.

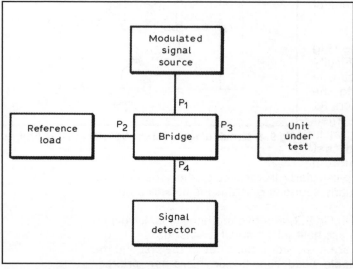

Fig 9.4: General setup of the bridge.

In the second method, the whole assembly is fitted to the lid of the diecast box, with a copper-clad fibreglass board fitted within the raised edge of the lid. In this form, it is easier to make good connections between the board and the four sockets which may be soldered in position.

In order to test the bridge, connect a modulated RF signal to port P1, via socket PL1. Connect an audio detector to PL4. Then, with two reference 50Ω loads connected to PL2 and PL3, check that the output detector reads a very low value. If there is any significant output (assuming the wiring is correct), fit a small capacitor close to either PL2 or PL3 as indicated by C_A or C_B in the circuit. The values of these should be adjusted to obtain balance and reduce any residual signal. Once balance has been obtained, the next step is to remove one of the two reference load resistors from PL2 or PL3. When this is done, the detected output should rise by about 30dB. If the reference loads PL2 and PL3 are interchanged, no difference should be detected.

For a 50Ω bridge it is useful to have one or two fixed-value mismatch loads available. A 75Ω load will give a VSWR of 1.5:1 and a 25Ω load will give a VSWR of 2:1. A short-circuit will give an infinite VSWR.

Operation of the bridge is readily appreciated from the general setup shown in **Fig 9.4**. If identical loads are connected to PL2 and PL3, the signals will be equal and in phase, so that no output will be detected at PL4. When the item under test at PL3 is different from that of the reference load, a difference signal is observed at PL4. Its magnitude is proportional to the difference.

The bridge resistors R1 and R2 are shown as 50Ω in the bridge. However, 75Ω could be used if a bridge was required for a 75Ω system.

DIP METER

Another very useful item in any antenna experimenter's shack is a dip meter. These pieces of equipment are given a variety of different names depending upon the type of amplifying device used in them. Early meters using valves were called grid dip meters (or oscillators (GDO)), whereas later meters using FETs altered the name slightly to gate dip oscillator. However, they may even be called FET dip oscillators and there may be other names as well for ordinary bipolar transistor meters. But, whatever they are called, they are essentially the same piece of equipment.

A dip meter or dip oscillator is an instrument that contains an oscillator that can be tuned over a wide range of frequencies. Generally, there are several ranges which can be chosen by the use of external plug-in coils. Their operation depends upon the fact that when a tank or tuned circuit of an oscillator is placed close to another resonant circuit the oscillator current will drop when tuned to the resonant frequency of the external circuit. By doing this, it is possible to check the resonant frequency of almost any tuned circuit regardless of whether it is on a circuit board or whether it forms part of an antenna. Thus a dip oscillator is essentially a form of calibrated variable frequency oscillator in which it is possible to monitor the oscillator current. It is worth noting that, by the very nature of the dip meter, its accuracy is very limited. This is because its resonant circuit is coupled into other circuits and this is bound to change the resonant frequency. Accordingly values of 10% would be considered to be very good. Often, the actual point of dip can be measured using a wide-band receiver to check the frequency of the oscillator at dip. Even then, the dip may not be particularly sharp, making exact location difficult. Nevertheless, the meter is indispensable in providing an easy way of locating resonant points.

Apart from acting as an oscillator, a meter usually has the facility to turn the oscillator off so that it can be used as an absorption wavemeter. In this mode, it can be used to pick up strong signals, like the RF field near a transmitter or feeder carrying RF power. In this form it is very useful for checking the frequency band of a transmission.

It can be seen that a dip meter can be used in a number of different ways. By using a little ingenuity, it can be used to perform a great variety of measurements which are very useful when setting up and experimenting with antennas.

In view of the rather specialised nature of dip meters, they are not always available from the normal electronic component and equipment stockists, and the variety that is available is much less than it was a few years ago. In cases where there are problems in locating them from the general outlets, it is worth trying local amateur radio dealers. Even if they do not have one themselves then they will almost certainly be able to advise where to obtain one.

G3WPO FET dip oscillator

The first version of the very successful G3WPO design appeared in *Radio Communication* in 1981 and the revised version appeared in 1987. The meter provides both wavemeter and dip functions, it covers 0.8 to 170MHz, gives audio and meter indications and is run from a battery.

The G3WPO Mk2 FET dip oscillator.

The circuit is shown in **Fig 9.5**. The instrument is based on a kalitron oscillator which is formed by two MOSFETS TR1 and TR2. The frequency-determining components are C1 and L1 (the plug-in coil). Resistors are included as part of the plug-in coil assembly and provide the gain setting for the circuit. The RF from the oscillator is detected by the Schottky barrier diodes D2 and D3. These have a good frequency response and a lower forward voltage drop than the ubiquitous 1N914. The detected DC is applied to the base of amplifier TR5 which controls the current flowing through the meter, M, and the mulivibrator formed by TR3 and TR4. C10/R18 and C11/R19 determine the frequency of the multivibrator.

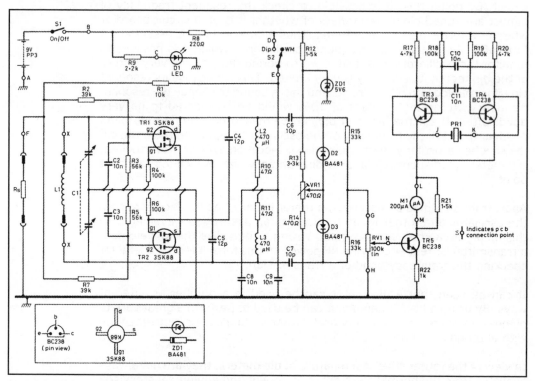

Fig 9.5: Circuit diagram of the FET dip oscillator.

As the current through TR5 increases, the note from the piezoelectric resonator increases, as does the meter reading. The meter and audio levels are set by the sensitivity control, RV1. The multivibrator commences oscillation at about the mid-scale on the meter and has a steadily detectable note that drops sharply as resonance of the RF circuit is reached.

Parts list

R1	10k	C1	Toko Polyvaricon, 2 x 266pF
R2, R7	39k	C2, C3, C8, C9	10n, 50V ceramic
R3, R5	56k	C4, C5	12p, 5% ceramic disc
R4, R6, R18, R19	100k	C6, C7	10p, 5% ceramic disc
R8	220	C10, C11	10n mylar
R9	2.2k	D1	3mm red LED
R10, R11	47	ZD1	5.6V, 400mW Zener
R12, R21	1.5k	TR1, TR2	3SK88
R13	3.3k	TR3 - TR5	BC238 or similar npn
R14	470	L1	See text for details
R15, R16	33k	L2, L3	470µH, eg Toko 7BS
R22	1k	M1	200µA meter
VR1	470 vert mount	S2	SPST switch
RV1 / S1	100k lin / switch	PR1	Piezo resonator, Toko PB2720

Shaft coupler	6:1 slow-motion drive
Wire,	0.2mm-diam enamelled copper
Nuts and bolts	various
5-pin DIN	plugs and sockets - see text
PP3 battery connector	

Table 9.1: Components list (all resistors are 0.25W, 5%)

In use as an absorption wavemeter, S2 removes the voltage supply to the oscillator. The received signal is then rectified by D2 and D3 and applied to the meter drive / audio circuits which are still powered. There is an increase in the meter reading and audio frequency as resonance is reached.

The circuit runs from a 9V supply (eg PP3 battery) with R8 acting as a current-limiting resistor. The current consumption between bands varies between 5 and 15mA. LED D1 acts as a reminder to show the unit is switched on.

Construction is relatively straight forward, although some skill in constructional techniques is required. Mechanical details of the case are given in **Fig 9.6** and details for the dial plate, cursor and scale are shown in **Fig 9.7**. The wiring details are shown in **Fig 9.8**. The PCB design is given in **Fig 9.9** and the component layout is shown in **Fig 9.10**.

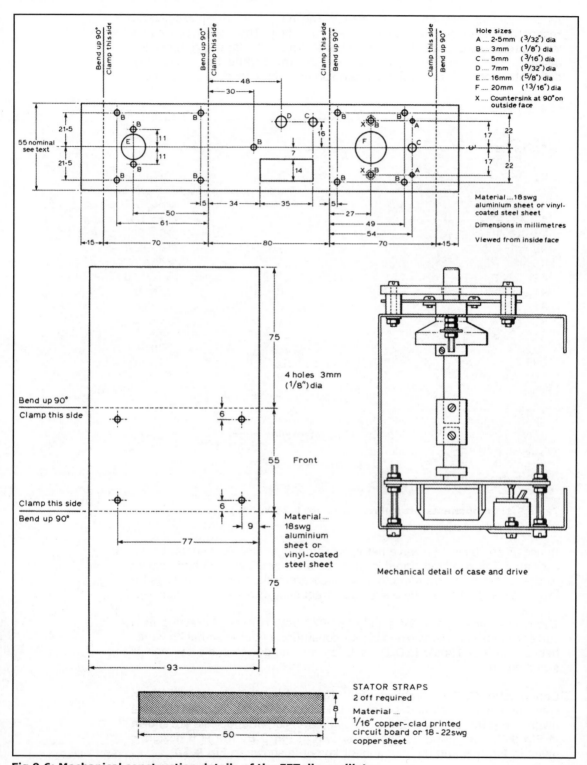

Fig 9.6: Mechanical construction details of the FET dip oscillator.

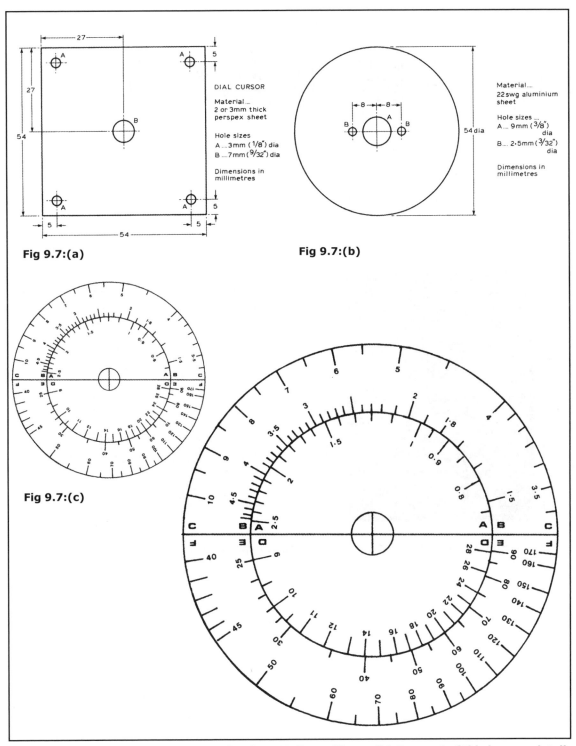

Fig 9.7:(a)

DIAL CURSOR

Material....
2 or 3mm thick
perspex sheet

Hole sizes
A ....3mm (1/8") dia
B ....7mm (9/32") dia

Dimensions in
millimetres

Fig 9.7:(b)

Material....
22 swg aluminium
sheet

Hole sizes ....
A .... 9mm (3/8")
dia
B.... 2·5mm (3/32")
dia

Dimensions in
millimetres

Fig 9.7:(c)

Fig 9.7: (a) Dial cursor and dial plate for the FET dip oscillator; (b) One part of this in more detail;
(c) Scale disc and enlargement to show details.

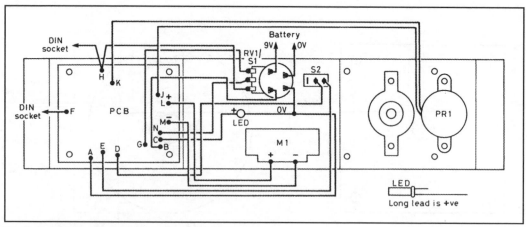

Fig 9.8: Wiring diagram for the FET dip oscillator.

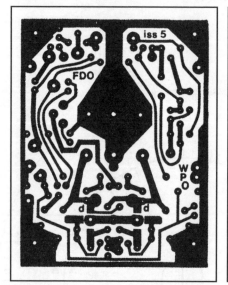

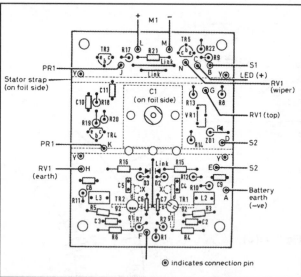

Fig 9.9: PCB layout for the FET dip oscillator.

Fig 9.10: Component layout for the FET dip oscillator.

There are five coils requiring construction. The coil assemblies are made by fitting 5-pin DIN audio plugs into rigid electrical plastic conduit to act as the former for the coil wire. Details of the construction of the coils are given in **Fig 9.11**. Only the actual plug end of the DIN plug is used, and this is glued into the end of the plastic tube. Coils for the lowest four ranges are wound directly onto the formers, whilst the two highest ranges are wound within the former which then acts as a protective shroud.

Once construction is complete, the unit can be checked for basic correct operation. When it is operating correctly, it can be calibrated. This is best performed by listening for the signal on a general-coverage receiver or scanner.

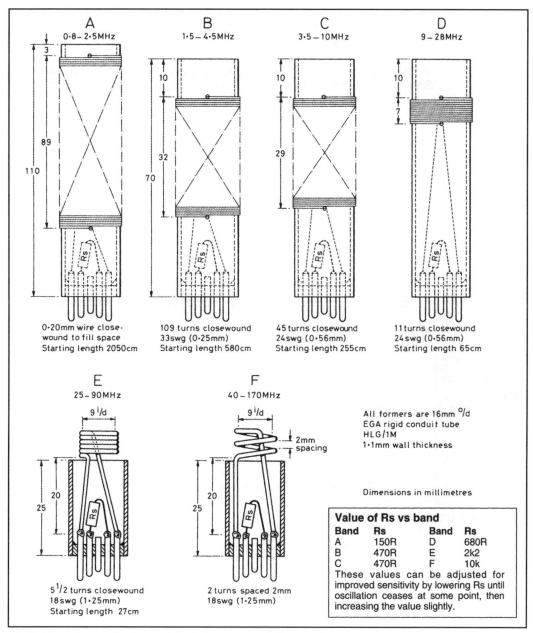

Fig 9.11: Coil construction details for the FET dip oscillator.

Measuring antenna resonant frequencies

This is probably the most obvious use for a dip meter in connection with an antenna. However, it is not necessarily one of the easiest measurement to make as there are several pitfalls.

In common with other measurements of the resonant frequency of a tuned circuit, the basic idea is to couple the coil of the oscillator to the circuit under test. When the oscillator is tuned to the resonant frequency of the antenna, the meter current will dip. The centre of the dip indicates the resonant frequency of the antenna.

When performing this measurement, it is best to perform it at the antenna itself and not via a feeder. While performing it via a feeder may seem perfectly in order, it is found that the feeder will introduce a number of spurious dips and it may be difficult to identify the correct response.

When checking the antenna, some way of coupling the oscillator to the antenna must be found. For an antenna in the HF section of the spectrum, it is possible to take a loop of two or three turns from the feed-point of the antenna and loop this over the coil of the dip meter. It may even be possible to use this method having a single turn loop at the low end of the VHF portion of the spectrum but, as the frequency rises, it may introduce some inaccuracies. The best way, if sufficient coupling can be obtained, is to short out the feed-point and place the coil as close as

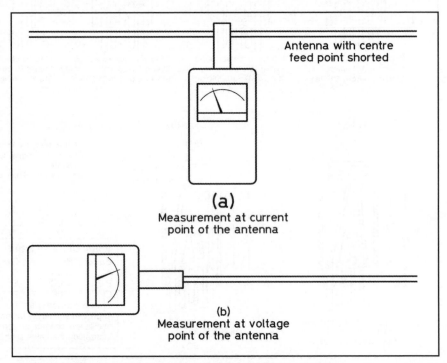

Fig 9.12: Measuring the resonant frequency of an antenna.

possible to the antenna as shown in **Fig 9.12**. It will be found that the best dip using the method of Fig 9.12(a) is at a current maximum (ie at the feed-point of most antennas). If the method of Fig 9.12(b) is used, the best dip will be obtained at a point of voltage maximum. This can always be found at the end of an antenna.

2·36 / 1·18 / 0·59

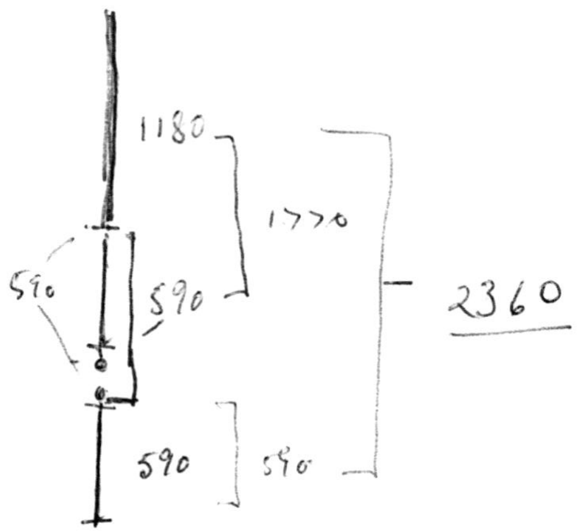

2360

1180

1770

590

590

590

590

127 MHz

436 MHz

$\frac{300}{436}$

$\frac{700}{\cancel{300}}\ \frac{680}{21}$

175

175 — 175

350

175

700

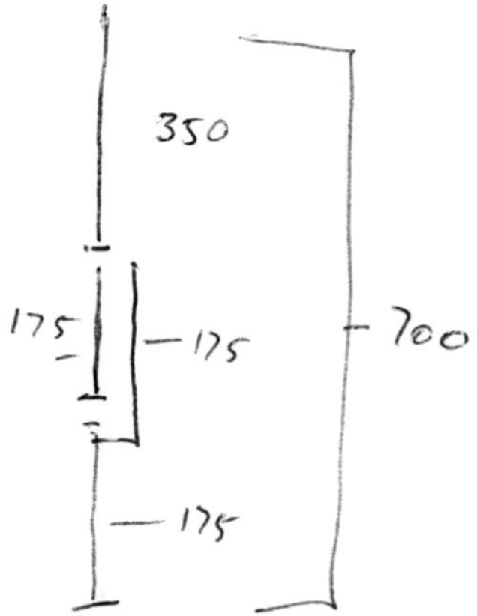

Measuring the electrical length of a feeder

A dip meter provides an easy method of measuring the electrical length of a piece of feeder. A knowledge of this length can be of value in a number of applications, especially if the antenna installation is used for transmitting.

In order to make the measurement, the feeder must be disconnected from the antenna and left open circuit. The other end should then be coupled to the dip meter as shown in **Fig 9.13**. Then, with the meter in its oscillator mode, it should be tuned from its lowest frequency upwards until a dip is observed. This frequency should be noted as it is the primary resonant frequency. However, it is wise to check this by tuning further up in frequency to the next few dips. These are harmonics of the fundamental resonance and they should be at multiples of the frequency of the first dip. If all is correct, the frequency of the first dip corresponds to a quarter-wavelength in the cable.

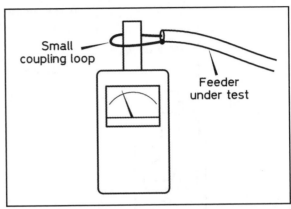

Fig 9.13: Using a dip meter to measure the electrical length of a feeder.

Feeder Impedance

It is also possible to measure the impedance of a length of feeder. This can be very useful if a length of unknown coax is to hand. Usually it is 50Ω for most cable used in amateur radio applications, but 75Ω is used for domestic TV and radio, and other impedances are used for computer applications. If spare lengths of feeder are to be used for amateur applications, it is necessary to know the impedance.

The method involves taking the length of coax and finding the dip for its resonance as in the measurement above. A variable resistor should then be attached to the remote end as shown in **Fig 9.14**. This resistor *must*

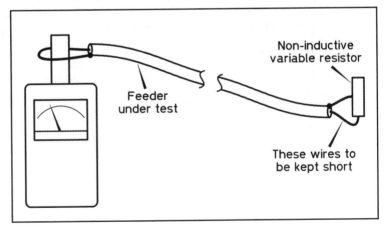

Fig 9.14: Using a dip meter to measure the characteristic impedance of a feeder.

not be wire-wound and it should have a value above the expected impedance for the feeder. For example, a 250Ω or 500Ω variable resistor would be suitable for most applications. In order to ensure the accuracy of the measurement, the connections to the variable resistor should be as short as possible. If they are too long, there is the possibility that some stray reactance will be added into the circuit and this could alter the readings.

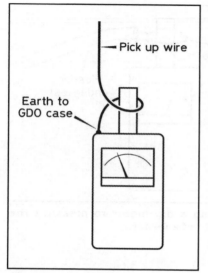

Fig 9.15: Using a dip meter as a field-strength meter.

At this point, the resistor should be varied until the dip meter is accurately tuned. The value of the resistor then corresponds to the characteristic impedance of the feeder. It should then be carefully removed and its resistance measured using a standard multimeter.

Using a dip meter as a field-strength meter

Apart from being used in its oscillator mode, a dip meter can also find a number of uses in its wavemeter mode. For this it is used to pick up the signal transmitted from the antenna, so this is really a measurement suitable for transmitting installations only.

As the meter in its wavemeter mode is comparatively insensitive, it will need to have a pickup wire or small antenna attached to it if it is to be placed at a reasonable distance away from the antenna. This can be set up as shown in **Fig 9.15**. The best performance will be obtained if the pickup wire is approximately $\lambda/4$ long. Then, the meter can be tuned to the correct frequency and the measurements and adjustments can be made to the antenna.

It should be noted that if high powers and antenna gains are involved, the antenna should not be approached when the power is on as this can present a safety hazard.

NOISE BRIDGES

Noise bridges provide a convenient method of measuring the impedance of an antenna. They are based around the popular Wheatstone bridge circuit. The basic idea of the noise bridge is shown in **Fig 9.16**. Rather than just using a simple DC source, here an AC source is used as it is required to measure values at different frequencies. This does not

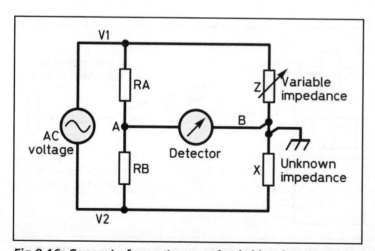

Fig 9.16: Concept of an antenna noise bridge for measuring antenna impedance. The AC source is normally a wide-band noise generator and the detector is a receiver set to the frequency at which the impedance is being measured.

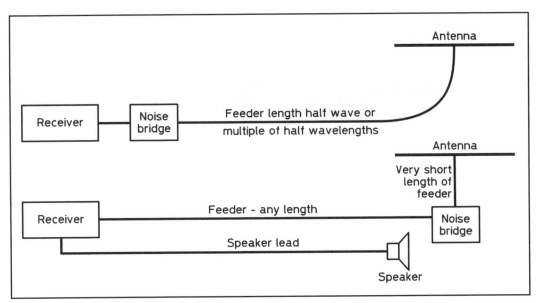

Fig 9.17: Operation of a noise bridge.

alter the fact that, as with any Wheatstone bridge, balance is obtained when the voltages at points A and B are the same. As RA and RB are chosen to be the same in this instance, balance will be obtained when Z is the same as X. With X being the unknown impedance of the antenna which can be complex, consisting of a resistance and a reactance, Z should also be capable of having variable resistance and reactance.

It is obviously necessary to check the operation of the antenna (see, for example, **Fig 9.17**) at a variety of frequencies. This would require a signal generator capable of operating over the band. There is no need for the signal to be on a single frequency. In fact it is a distinct advantage for it to generate a signal over a wide band of frequencies. In this way, it is only necessary to adjust the frequency of the detector, which in this case is a receiver. As a result the AC source should be a noise generator. It is therefore possible to adjust the noise bridge for the minimum level of noise on the received frequency (ie the bridge balance condition) to determine the impedance of the antenna.

The solution appears to be particularly simple. The noise bridge is ideal in that it provides a direct reading of the antenna impedance. Unfortunately there are a couple of drawbacks. The first is that these instruments are not particularly accurate. This generally results from the fact that the bridge network is relatively complicated and stray inductance and capacitance will be present, especially at VHF and UHF. The other disadvantage is that the bridge will only see the correct impedance when connected directly to the antenna, or when fed by a length of feeder a multiple of half wavelengths long. Normally the bridge is connected directly to the antenna, but the detector (receiver) will normally be located in the shack. To overcome this, a pair of headphones or small speaker can be connected to the receiver via a suitable length of wire so that it can be heard at the antenna.

REFERENCE

[1]   *Test Equipment for the Radio Amateur* 3rd Edition, Clive Smith, G4FZH, RSGB, 1995.

Chapter 10
Practical Aspects

The performance of the antenna itself is naturally exceedingly important. However, its installation and positioning also play a vital role in the overall performance of the whole system. An antenna mounted in one location may give a disappointing account of itself, whereas one positioned in a different location may produce outstanding results. Positioning may also affect aspects such as the electromagnetic compatibility (EMC) performance of the station. Located in one position, the station may cause interference to other electronic equipment such as hi-fi systems and televisions. By careful location of the antenna, it may be possible to avoid many of these problems. Similarly, many problems of interference caused by other pieces of electronic equipment can be reduced.

Other aspects of the installation of the antenna are also important. Choice of the correct materials and installation techniques can have a major impact on long term reliability and safety. Correctly installed, an antenna can last for many years. A poorly installed one may fail or even fall down after a relatively short period.

CHOICE OF LOCATION
One of the first decisions to make for any antenna is where to locate it. The available choices may even impact the choice of the basic antenna itself. There are many places where antennas can be mounted. Some may be located in the house, possibly within the attic or loft space. Others may be mounted to the side of the house, or a chimney. However, some people will install a tower or mast especially for the antenna. Wherever the antenna is located, the height is one aspect that affects the performance to a considerable degree.

Antenna height
There are many aspects that should be considered when deciding upon the height at which the antenna should be mounted. It is generally found that the higher it is, the greater the cost in installing it. A taller mast may be required, and longer feeders will be needed. Long feeders may also reduce the effectiveness of any gain achieved in increasing the height. However significant levels of gain can be achieved by mounting antennas as high as is reasonably possible.

For optimum performance, the antenna should be mounted above any local objects so that they do not screen it. A working value of 12m or 40ft is a very good general guide, because this tends to take the antenna above the layer of electrical interference and also above signal variations caused (at higher frequencies) by the heat layer above buildings. It may also help reduce EMC problems as described later.

If there is no screening by buildings, and assuming the antenna is over ground that is flat for several miles around, the main lobe of the radiation at low levels will tend to be raised in the vertical plane. As the antenna height increases, the direction of the main lobe will reduce in elevation. Although the performance will be affected by such things as minor lobes, usually there is an increase in gain as the height is increased. As a general rule, there is about a 6dB gain for every doubling in the height of the antenna. For example, when using an antenna on a 12m mast, assuming this clears all obstacles, using the antenna on a 24m mast would give a signal increase of 6dB. This assumes that the additional length of feeder required does not introduce any loss. In a real installation this would need to be taken into consideration.

This is only a very general case. Should the antenna be mounted on a hill, increasing its height is unlikely to give any real improvement. Instead the effective height should relate to the bottom of the hill. Conversely an antenna mounted in a valley will achieve much greater levels of signal increase as a more favourable angle to the nearby hill top is achieved. However, be aware that the signal in some directions may be enhanced by reflections from buildings or the side of a valley, and a height increase may occasionally decrease the signal in some directions.

Internal antenna systems

While most people will want to mount an antenna outside the house, this is not always possible. Many people live in flats where it may not be possible to install an external antenna. Also, many houses these days have covenants that prevent the use of external antennas. It may be that it is just more convenient to locate the antenna inside. This will have the advantage that the antenna does not have to be built to the standards required to withstand the rigours of the weather, and cable routing as well as direction control may be easier.

When mounting an antenna inside, it should be remembered that there is a noticeable loss in performance when compared with an externally-mounted antenna. The roofing materials tend to shade or screen the antenna. It is difficult to assess the level of attenuation, but it could be more than 6dB, and this rises with higher frequencies. The level of attenuation is increased further when the tiles are wet Fortunately, slates dry out fairly quickly, but the more porous varieties of tile will remain wet, and their losses will remain high for longer, as they do not dry out as quickly. These losses can vary by 7dB and more between wet and dry conditions at 430MHz.

Care should also be taken when siting the antenna internally. Internal wiring (eg mains electricity) may cause the antenna to become de-tuned and result in its performance being degraded. Much of the wiring may not be immediately visible. Also in a loft or attic there will be a water tank and this will have a considerable effect. Additionally, any wiring may pick up large amounts of the transmitted signal and this may give rise to interference. Care must be taken to avoid this as much as possible

Chimney mounting
A chimney on the house can provide an excellent point at which to mount the antenna. However, before making a final decision, it is necessary to make sure that the antenna will not overlap a neighbour's property. It should be lashed to the chimney in two or three places and a short fixed mast used to clear the chimney. A rotator can be placed above this for a rotatable antenna.

When considering the size of antenna to be erected, take a look at the wind loading and turning circle. This may limit the size of antenna to be considered. However if in any doubt a survey of the chimney should be undertaken by a qualified person. This may prevent a potentially dangerous and very expensive collapse later.

Accessibility should also be considered. If the chimney is not very accessible, this may limit the size of antenna that can be installed. Access for maintenance should also be considered.

When installing the antenna, only the proper fixings should be used. For lightweight antennas, ordinary TV fixings can be used but, for larger antenna systems, heavyweight fixings can be obtained from amateur radio suppliers.

Mast and towers
In many instances, people will want to use a mast or a tower, and many varieties are available. Some are free-standing, whereas others may be wall-mounted. If the facility to raise and lower the mast or tower is available, this can give the flexibility to experiment with antennas. The most convenient location can also be chosen. However, masts and towers are more expensive to buy and more time-consuming to install. Also in the UK, planning permission is almost invariably required before they can be installed, and this may also be the case in other areas of the world. It is always wise to check on the requirements in the earliest stages of planning an antenna system.

While many towers are free-standing, guyed masts may provide a good solution. They are cheaper than self-supporting towers, but guys naturally take up more space and may require a larger garden. In addition to this, considerable care is required in erecting them, especially when they are loaded with antennas.

Photo: A large antenna system mounted on a tower.

A further requirement for a tower or mast is that lightning protection should be installed. A very good earth is required along with wide copper straps from the mast to the earth connection. In this way, current flowing into the house wiring will be reduced in the event of an incident. In view of the importance of this protection, professional advice should be sought.

CHOICE OF MATERIALS FOR ANTENNA INSTALLATIONS

The choice of materials and particularly metals used in an antenna system can have a great effect on the way in which the atmosphere affects the system. The use of dissimilar metals will cause considerable trouble as a result of electrolytic action. This arises because each metal has its own electro-potential. Unless metals with similar potentials are used, the difference in potential will mean that corrosion results, even when they are dry. If moisture is present, the effect is greatly increased, and this is further worsened when atmospheric pollution is present. If it is absolutely necessary that dissimilar metals are used, great care must be made to reduce the effect to a minimum by ensuring that all moisture is excluded.

Metals can be arranged in the electrochemical series to determine the extent of the effect. If metals are close together in the series, the corrosion effects will be less, whereas if metals are further apart in the series, the effect will be much greater. Metals in the lower part of the series will corrode those in the upper part. For example, brass or copper screws that are in the lower half of the series will corrode an aluminium tube, because aluminium is in the upper half. However, cadmium plated screws would cause less corrosion.

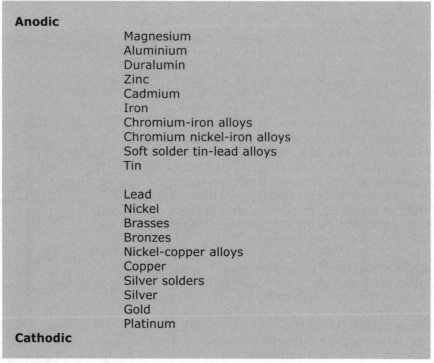

Anodic

Magnesium
Aluminium
Duralumin
Zinc
Cadmium
Iron
Chromium-iron alloys
Chromium nickel-iron alloys
Soft solder tin-lead alloys
Tin

Lead
Nickel
Brasses
Bronzes
Nickel-copper alloys
Copper
Silver solders
Silver
Gold
Platinum

Cathodic

Table 10.1: The electrochemical series for metals.

Corrosion not only causes a reduction in the strength of a mechanical structure, but it will also make it less easy to dismantle when the need arises. It can also increase contact resistance between elements and feeders. This occurs because many antenna elements are aluminium and feeders are generally copper. This can result in joints becoming corroded and presenting a high resistance where power is dissipated, thereby reducing the efficiency of the antenna.

Under some instances the corroded materials can act as semiconductor devices providing a non-linear component that can generate harmonics and intermodulation products. This is often known as the 'rusty bolt' effect. Signals generated in this way can affect other users, both in and out of the amateur band. As a result, it is necessary to select materials to minimise corrosion, keep moisture away from any areas where dissimilar materials need to be used, and inspect and refurbish antennas and their weather protection measures at least every two years.

WIND LOADING
Before any antenna system is erected, consideration should be given to the wind loading. Large antennas and masts present a significant area to any wind that may be blowing, and the resulting forces can be significant. Wind survivability is often quoted for masts and rotators. These figures should be studied carefully to ensure that the complete system, when it is installed, will not fall outside the specification of any of the constituents. A complete summary of wind loading is given in [1].

STACKING ANTENNAS
In view of the cost of a mast or a tower, and the space occupied, it is often necessary to mount more than one antenna on the mast. For example, antennas may be required for different bands. It is also possible to stack antennas for the same band and feed them in phase to provide additional gain. When doing this, the antennas should be spaced by a minimum of half the boom length. A feed arrangement like that described in the 'Feeders' chapter should be used.

When using antennas for two bands, the one for the higher frequency band is normally placed at the top. This places less strain on the mast as the antenna with the lower wind resistance will be at the top. As a rule of thumb, the minimum spacing between the two antennas should be half the length of the boom of the upper antenna. If closer spacing than this is required, the feed impedance will be changed and it may be necessary to adjust any gamma or other matching device to accommodate this.

If it is possible to achieve a wider spacing than this, better results can be achieved. It has been previously shown that the impedance of an antenna varies with its height above ground. In the case of two stacked antennas, the lower one appears like ground to the higher one. At points half a wavelength or a multiple of a half-wavelength above ground, the impedance passes through its nominal or free-space value. This means that the antenna impedance will be correct at this spacing.

In addition to this, the lower antenna will act as a reflector or ground plane for the upper one. Again, at multiples of a half-wavelength, the

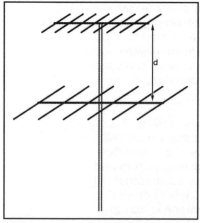

Figure 10.1: Stacking one Yagi antenna above another. The minimum distance, d, should be about half the boom length of the smaller antenna.

effect is such that a low angle of radiation is achieved. It is worth noting that for odd multiples of a quarter-wavelength there is a considerable amount of high-angle radiation.

AVOIDING INTERFERENCE

Even today, with manufactured equipment having to pass stringent EMC regulations, there is still the possibility of interference arising, especially when high-power transmitters are used. Sensitive amateur receivers can also be affected by the noise generated by domestic equipment whether they be lawn mowers, power drills, computers or a whole host of other pieces of everyday electrical and electronic apparatus.

While there is no guarantee that interference can be avoided, there are a few simple rules that can be followed to help ensure that the risk of suffering from interference (or causing it) can be significantly reduced.

- Use coaxial feeders that provide high levels of screening, especially for runs that are indoors or near other electrical or electronic apparatus.
- Use baluns or chokes when feeding balanced antennas with coaxial feeder to ensure that RF does not radiate from the outer of the feeder, or is picked up by it.
- Place the amateur antennas as far away as possible from other antennas and equipment. Remember that telephone lines can act as excellent 'antennas' for interference, even into the VHF and UHF regions. Mains wiring, speaker leads and other cabling can also pick up significant levels of signal.
- When installing an antenna, ensure that all metals used are electrochemically similar to prevent corrosion that might lead to the 'rusty bolt' effect.
- Overhaul antennas to ensure that corrosion has not become a problem
- Avoid running feeders parallel to mains cabling. Even though the coax is well screened, sufficient levels of power can be picked up by the mains cable to result in interference to other equipment.
- Avoid beaming transmitting antennas at receiving antennas (eg television antennas) as the receiving equipment may become overloaded, resulting in interference.
- Avoid having antennas close in the same plane. It can be found that raising or lowering one of the antennas by even a few feet can considerably reduce the levels of interference.

SAFETY

Antennas, and masts and towers in particular, are potentially very dangerous, especially when they are being erected or dismantled. This means that safety is of paramount importance. A little prior thought, and a few precautions should prevent any accidents occurring. While very few people are injured as a result of the hobby, there have been some serious accidents in the past. Fortunately, if care is taken, these accidents should be avoided, enabling the hobby to be enjoyed safely.

Safety precautions take many forms. One of the first is that under no circumstances should an antenna be erected where there is any possibility of it falling on power lines, or power lines falling on to the antenna. This may seem a remote possibility, but people have been killed in the past as a result of this happening.

At all times, the proper materials and fixings should be used. Do not take any short cuts because falling antennas can cause serious injury. For smaller antennas, standard television fixings can be used, but for anything that is slightly larger, obtain them from amateur radio dealers.

If in doubt about how to install something, seek professional advice. While this may add to the cost of the antenna, it is worth it in the long run. If the antenna falls down it can cost considerably more than the advice.

When planning to erect an antenna system, the job should be well planned. Considerations must include the positioning of every part of the antenna and the mast, and at every stage of the process. Ensure there are enough people and make sure that have the correct protective clothing - boots, gloves, and safety helmets. When dealing with towers and masts, make sure that sufficient guy ropes are used to give control as the system is raised. It is also necessary to make sure that nobody can trip over the guy ropes.

Never attempt to carry out any work on an antenna during windy conditions. Even if there is a deadline to meet, such as the start of a contest, the risk is not worth taking. While amateur radio is a great hobby, it only a hobby and it is not worth taking any major risks.

Before raising or lowering a system, double-check that all components and fastenings are firm and safe. The base of a mast must be checked to ensure there is no chance of it slipping.

If several people are involved in erecting an antenna system, make sure everyone knows his role. In this way, the operation should run smoothly and there should not be any of the "I thought you were doing that" type of instances. Also, make sure there that anyone not involved in the job keeps well clear and out of the area where the antenna could fall if the worst were to happen. This applies particularly to any children. Animals should also be kept well clear and under control.

One person should be in charge of the operation, and he should not have any active part in the lifting activities. In this way, he can gain a good view of the whole activity and make sure it all goes according to plan. Any instructions he gives must be clear and concise to prevent any misinterpretation.

Once the antenna system is in place, check all the fixings to make sure they are secure. Then clear up the site removing any temporary ropes and equipment.

Even for what may appear to be a simple one-man job, make sure that no chances are taken. Above all, ensure that someone is on site to call for assistance if the worst does happen.

After the antenna system has been installed, it needs to be checked periodically for wear, safety and performance. The rigours of the weather will attack even the best antenna systems. A periodic check, at least every two years, should be undertaken to ensure that everything is satisfactory. Be prepared to replace any parts that have worn or are badly corroded.

These are just a few points that should be noted when installing an antenna system. Every eventuality cannot be considered here. The best way to ensure that everything runs safely is to be aware of any safety risks all the time. Never take any risks; it is not worth it if there is risk of injury, especially to someone else. Think how the system will be erected and find ways of overcoming any risks. Also ensure that, once the system is installed, it will remain there intact, even during storms. The old adage "if the antenna did not fall down it was not big enough" is nonsense. Not only does this risk safety, but the success of an antenna should be judged by its availability. If it is not available for use because it has fallen down, this is surely a measure of failure.

While many of these precautions may appear to be extreme, they have been learned the hard way by many people. By ensuring that an antenna system is safely put into place, we can make the most of this excellent hobby.

REFERENCES AND FURTHER READING

[1]   'Wind Loading', D J Reynolds, G3ZPF, *Radio Communication* April 1988, pp252 - 55 and May 1988, pp340 - 41.
[2]   *The RSGB Guide to EMC*, Robin Page-Jones, G3JWI, RSGB 1998.

Index

VHF/UHF ANTENNAS

Other books by **Ian Poole**

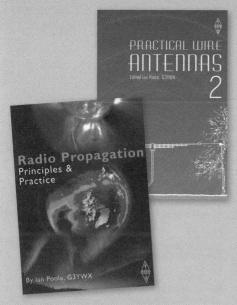

Practical Wire Antennas 2

"Probably the best book on wire antennas ever"

Practical Wire Antennas 2 provides a collection of antenna designs and ideas that will help capture the enjoyment of experimenting in the true spirit of amateur radio. This book will help improve any station and is a must have book for anyone interested in antenna construction.

176 pages, 240 x 175mm, paperback ISBN: 1-905086-04-0

Price £11.99

Radio Propagation - Principles & Practice

This book provides the reader with a practical understanding of Radio Propagation so that they can use them to their best. *Radio Propagation - Practice and Principles* is an essential read for anyone associated with radio communications.

Size: 174x240 mm, 112 pages, ISBN: 1-872309-97-6

Price £14.99

HF Amateur Radio

The HF (or short wave) bands are one of the most interesting areas of amateur radio. Stations from all around the globe can be heard and many interesting contacts can be made. Operating on these frequencies requires many skills if the most is to be made of the time that is available.

HF Amateur Radio will benefit those new to amateur radio, anyone contemplating exploring the world below 30MHz, and just about any licensed amateur or short-wave listener who feels he could get more out of his station.

Size 240x174 mm, 144 pages, ISBN 9781-9050-8629-0

Price £12.99

Amateur Radio Explained
A Guide to Getting Started in Ham Radio

This book provides the ideal introduction to the wonderful world of amateur radio. *Amateur Radio Explained* is for people first taking an interest in amateur radio and those ready to move on from foundation level. *Amateur Radio Explained* is the perfect introduction to the exciting world of amateur radio. But be warned: you may become hooked for life!

Size 210x297mm, 80 pages, ISBN 9781-9050-8632-0

Price £5.79

Radio Society of Great Britain

3 Abbey Court, Fraser Road, Priory Business Park, Bedford MK44 3WH Tel: 01234 832 700 Fax: 01234 831 496

www.rsgbshop.org

RSGB SHOP

Other **RSGB** Books

TRAINING

IEXM	International Amateur Radio Exam Manual	£14.99
FNOW	Foundation Licence - NOW!	£4.99
IMED	Intermediate Licence Book	£6.99
ADVA	Advance! The Full Licence Manual	£11.99

BEGINNERS

AREX	Amateur Radio Explained	£5.79
HRFD	Ham Radio for Dummies	£14.99

SHORT WAVE LISTING

USG3	Radio Today Ultimate Scanning Guide	£19.99
LBRX	Log Book - Receiving	£4.99

MORSE CODE

MCRA	Morse Code for Radio Amateurs	£7.99
INMC	Learning the Morse Code (CD)	£9.99

SPACE & SATELLITES

ARAS	Amateur Radio Astronomy	£16.99

IOTA

IDIR	IOTA Directory	£9.99

OPERATING & DX

WLOD	World Licensing and Operating Directory	£12.99
PRE8	RSGB Prefix Guide 8th Edition - **revised 2008**	£8.99
RADO	Radio Orienteering - ARDF Handbook	£9.99
OPM6	The RSGB Operating Manual 6th Edition	£19.99
RPPP	Propagation-Principles & Practice	£14.99
WHOS	Who's who in Amateur Radio	£14.99

ANTENNA BOOKS

AFVA	Antennas for VHF and above	£12.99
BSHA	Building Successful HF Antennas	£14.99
HFA2	HF Amateur Radio	£12.99
MVAC	More Vertical Antenna Classics	£13.99
PWA2	Practical Wire Antennas 2	£11.99
INAC	International Antenna Collection	£12.99
INA2	International Antenna Collection 2	£12.99
ANTO	Antenna Topics	£18.99
ATK2	Antenna Toolkit 2	£28.99
TAFE	The Antenna File	£18.99
BKYA	Backyard Antennas	£18.99
NACO	HF Antenna Collection	£19.99
HFAL	HF Antennas for all Locations	£19.99
TAEG	The Antenna Experimenters Guide	£17.99

TECHNICAL BOOKS

WEEK	Weekend Projects	£13.99
RADN	Radio Nature	£13.99
RG08	The Rig Guide (including p&p)	£3.99
RFDB	RF Design Basics	£17.99
PSHB	Power Supply Handbook	£15.99
PICB	Pic Basics	£14.99
CIRO	Circuit Overload	£14.99
ARES	Amateur Radio Essentials	£15.99
RCH9	The Radio Comms Handbook	£29.99
HART	25 years of Hart Reviews	£14.99
RFCC	RF Components & Circuits	£25.99
COMM	CoMmand	£16.99
PRAC	Practical Projects	£12.99
DMFO	Digital Modes for all Occasions	£16.99
TEC1	RSGB Technical Compendium	£17.99
RDRB	Radio Data Reference Book	£14.99
TT50	Technical Topics Scrapbook - All 50 years	£14.99
TTSB4	Technical Topics Scrapbook 2000-04	£14.99
TTSB3	Technical Topics Scrapbook 1995-99	£14.99
TTSB2	Technical Topics Scrapbook 1990-94	£13.99
TTSB	Technical Topics Scrapbook 1985-89	£9.99
PSCB	Power Supply Cookbook	£26.99
YGTP	Your Guide to Propagation	£9.99

LOW FREQUENCY

LFT2	LF Today NEW 2nd Edition	£12.99
LEHB	LF Experimenters Guide	£18.99

HISTORY BOOKS

ABOC	A Bit of Controversy	£13.99
PTCG	Perera's Telegraph Collectors Guide	£9.99
CAMM	FJ Camm - The Practical Man	£10.99
TSOE	The Story of Enigma (CD)	£9.99
TCCD	Perera's Telegraph Collectors CD	£9.99
BOXS	1940s Amateur Radio Set	£15.99
WATF	World at Their Fingertips	£9.99

VHF/UHF BOOKS

SMHB	6m Handbook	£13.99
VHF2	VHF/UHF Handbook	£19.99
YGUV	Guide to VHF/UHF	£8.99

LOW POWER (QRP)

MQRP	More QRP Power	£16.99
QRPB	QRP Basics	£14.99
LPSB	Low Power Scrapbook	£14.99

MICROWAVES

IMH2	International Microwave Handbook 2	£8.99
MICP	Microwave Projects 1	£14.99
MIP2	Microwave Projects 2	£14.99

E&OE All prices shown are plus p&p. All prices subject to change without notice.

RSGB SHOP ORDER FORM

PLEASE PRINT ALL

NAME

CALLSIGN/MEMBERSHIP NUMBER

ADDRESS

POSTCODE | | | | | | TELEPHONE

E-MAIL

QUANTITY	CODE	DESCRIPTION/TITLE	PRICE	TOTAL

PLEASE CHARGE MY CREDIT/DEBIT CARD | | | | | | | | | | | | | | | | | | | | | | | P&P

EXPIRY DATE | | | | | START DATE | | | | | CVV2* | | | | ISSUE NUMBER | | |

*3 DIGIT CODE FROM THE BACK OF YOUR CARD

Total

SIGNATURE

DATE | | | | | | | |

Order on the internet at **www.rsgbshop.org**. Cheques and postal orders crossed and made payable to Radio Society of Great Britain or telephone your credit card order to 01234 832 700. HQ open 8.30-4.30 (Mon-Fri). Send no cash. **Post & Packing:** UK £1.75 For 1 item, £3.30 For 2 or more items. Overseas: Air £9 for 1 item, £15 for 2 items & £3 for each extra item. Surface: £3.00 For 1 item, £5 for 2 items & £1.00 For each extra item.

Radio Society of Great Britain

3 Abbey Court, Fraser Road, Priory Business Park, Bedford MK44 3WH Tel: 01234 832 700 Fax: 01234 831 496 **E&OE**

www.rsgbshop.org